Revise A2 Physics for AQA Specification A

Harvey Cole
and
David Sang

Revise A2 Physics for AQA Specification A

Harvey Cole
and
David Sang

Heinemann

Heinemann Educational Publishers
Halley Court, Jordan Hill, Oxford, OX2 8EJ
Part of Harcourt Education

Heinemann is the registered trademark of Harcourt Education Limited

First published 2001

10-digit ISBN: 0 435581 99 6
13-digit ISBN: 978 0 435581 99 2

09 08 07 06
8 7 6 5 4 3 2 1

Development editor Paddy Gannon

Edited by Patrick Bonham

Typeset and illustrated by Saxon Graphics Ltd, Derby

Index compiled by Ann Hall

Printed and bound in the UK by Ashford Colour Press

Acknowledgements
The publishers have made every effort to trace the copyright holders, but if they
have inadvertently overlooked any, they will be pleased to make the necessary
arrangements at the first opportunity.

Tel: 01865 888058   www.heinemann.co.uk

Contents

Introduction – How to use this revision guide

This revision guide is designed to follow **Specification A** of the **AQA Physics A2** course and is divided into two modules to match the course. You may be taking an examination at the end of each module, or you may take all the examinations at the end of the course. The content is exactly the same.

This guide does not cover the work for the Practical Examination (or Practical Coursework) or the five options that make up Module 6.

Each module begins with an **introduction**, which summarises the content. It also reminds you of the topics from your GCSE course that the module draws on.

The content of each module is presented in **blocks**, to help you divide up your study into manageable chunks. Each block is dealt with in several spreads. These do the following:

- they **summarise** the content;
- they indicate **points to note**;
- they include **worked examples** of calculations;
- they include **diagrams** of the sort you might need to reproduce in examinations;
- they provide **hint boxes** to give you general hints about how to get the Physics right;
- they provide **quick check** questions to help you test your understanding.

At the end of each module, there are longer **end-of-module questions** similar in style to those you will encounter in tests. **Answers** to all questions are provided at the end of the book.

You need to understand the **scheme of assessment** for your course. This is summarised on page 3 opposite.

A note about units

In some of the worked examples, we have included units throughout the calculations. This can help to ensure that you end up with the correct units in your final answer.

In an examination it is not necessary to include the units in all steps of a calculation. Always include the units in the final answer.

Scheme of Assessment for A2 Physics

There are three **units of assessment** (Units 4, 5 and 6) in this A2 Physics course. Unit 5 includes assessment of **experimental skills**, and the assessment of whichever option you have studied in Module 6. Unit 6 is a **synoptic** paper. Synoptic means 'a general overview', and questions may be set that combine topics in modules 1 to 5.

Unit	Name	Duration of written test	Types of question	Weighting at A-level*
4	Waves, fields and nuclear energy	90 minutes	multiple choice (30 marks) short structured (30 marks)	15%
5	Nuclear instability and option module	75 minutes	structured (40 marks)	10%
+ *either*	Experimental skills	none	coursework (30 marks)	5%
or	Experimental skills	90 minutes	practical exam (30 marks)	5%
6	Synoptic paper	180 minutes	structured (80 marks)	20%

*The weighting is the percentage of the total A-level mark.

In **multiple choice questions** there are four responses, and you have to select the response which you think is the best answer.

Short structured questions require brief answers to several linked parts of a question.

Structured questions are similar to the short structured questions but some parts may require longer answers.

Your answers will be used to assess the quality of your **written communication**. Up to two marks in each paper will be awarded for your ability to

- select an appropriate style of writing,
- organise the information,
- use specialist vocabulary,
- write legibly, using accurate spelling, grammar and punctuation.

> In exams, use the mark allocation and the space available for your answer to guide how much you write.

Module 4: Waves, fields and nuclear energy

There are five blocks in this module.

- **Block 4A** is about oscillations and waves. It explains the characteristic features of simple harmonic motion and free and forced vibrations, and covers the properties of waves, building on work you may have done for GCSE. It shows how an understanding of waves can be used to explain polarisation, interference and diffraction.

- **Block 4B** is about capacitors and capacitance.

- **Block 4C** introduces ideas of circular motion and the theory of gravitational and electrical fields.

- **Block 4D** deals with the magnetic effects of electric currents, and electromagnetic induction.

- **Block 4E** shows how the concepts of binding energy and mass difference explain nuclear fusion and fission, and describes how induced fission is used in thermal nuclear reactors. Safety aspects of nuclear power are also covered.

Block 4A: Oscillations and waves, pages 6–23

Ideas from GCSE	Content outline of Block 4A
• Kinetic and potential energy	• Graphical and analytical treatment of SHM
• Longitudinal and transverse waves	• Resonance and damping
• Frequency, wavelength, amplitude and speed of a wave	• Longitudinal and transverse waves
• Diffraction of waves	• Polarisation of transverse waves
	• Displacement, amplitude, period, frequency, speed and phase difference
	• Stationary waves
	• Interference and diffraction

Block 4B: Capacitance, pages 24–27

Ideas from GCSE	Content outline of Block 4B
• Electric charge, voltage and energy	• Capacitance
• Relationship between current, voltage and resistance	• Energy stored by a capacitor
	• Charging and discharging capacitors

Block 4C: Gravitational and electrical fields, pages 28–41 and 54

Ideas from GCSE	Content outline of Block 4C
• Gravity and gravitational potential energy • The solar system, planets and satellites	• Uniform motion in a circle • Centripetal force • Newton's law of gravitation • Gravitational field strength and potential • Motion of planets and satellites • Electrical field strength and potential • Motion of charged particles in an electric field • Electric and gravitational fields compared

Block 4D: Magnetic effects of currents, pages 42–45

Ideas from GCSE	Content outline of Block 4D
• Electromagnets • The motor effect and the left-hand rule • Electromagnetic induction – factors affecting size of induced voltage	• Force on a current-carrying wire in a magnetic field • Motion of charged particles in a magnetic field • Magnetic flux density, flux and flux linkage • Electromagnetic induction – Faraday's and Lenz's laws

Block 4E: Nuclear applications, pages 46–53

Ideas from GCSE	Content outline of Block 4E
• Nuclear fission and chain reactions • Radiation hazards and safety	• Mass difference and binding energy • Induced fission and chain reactions • Thermal reactors and safety aspects • Artificial transmutation

End-of-module questions, pages 55–58

Simple harmonic motion

Start a pendulum swinging; pluck a stretched string; pull and release a mass on a spring. All of these result in **free oscillations**, in which a mass vibrates freely at its natural frequency. In many situations, these oscillations take the form of what is called **simple harmonic motion (SHM)**.

Displacement, amplitude, period, frequency

An oscillation can be represented by a displacement–time graph. An oscillation can be described using the following terms:

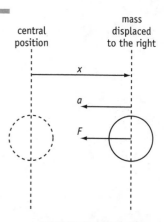

- **displacement** x: distance of the mass from its equilibrium position (metres, m)
- **amplitude** A: greatest value of the displacement (metres, m)
- **period** T: time for one complete oscillation (seconds, s)
- **frequency** f: number of oscillations per second (hertz, Hz)

Frequency and period are related by

$$f = \frac{1}{T} \quad \text{or} \quad T = \frac{1}{f}$$

Frequency is measured in **hertz (Hz)**. 1 Hz = 1 oscillation/s = 1 s^{-1}.

- 1 kHz (kilohertz) = 10^3 Hz
- 1 MHz (megahertz) = 10^6 Hz
- 1 GHz (gigahertz) = 10^9 Hz

> The frequency is the number of oscillations per second; the period is the number of seconds per oscillation.

✓ *Quick check 1, 2*

Defining SHM

Not all oscillations are simple harmonic. For SHM, a mass is displaced from a central position, where it is in equilibrium. A **restoring force** F acts in the opposite direction to the displacement x; for SHM, this force must be proportional to x. This gives the mass an acceleration a, towards the central position, that is proportional to x. Hence:

- Simple harmonic motion occurs when the acceleration of a mass is directed towards a fixed point and is proportional to its displacement from that point.

We can write this as an equation that involves the frequency f:

$$a = -(2\pi f)^2 x$$

✓ *Quick check 3*

The pendulum

The bob of a pendulum oscillates with SHM. The motion can be studied by connecting the arm of a pendulum to a rotary position sensor and datalogger. The time period depends on the length l but not on the mass (assuming the mass of the arm is very small).

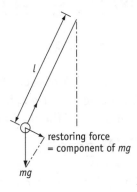

$$T = 2\pi\sqrt{\frac{l}{g}}$$

restoring force = component of mg

mg

The restoring force is gravity tending to return the bob to its lowest position.

Mass–spring system

Set a trolley oscillating horizontally between fixed supports. The time period T depends upon the trolley's mass m and the stiffness k of the springs. A greater mass gives less acceleration and a longer time; stiffer springs exert more restoring force, giving greater acceleration and a shorter period. The same is true for a vertical mass–spring system.

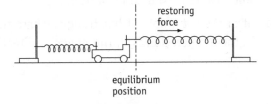

restoring force

equilibrium position

restoring force = $-kx$

equilibrium position

mg

$$T = 2\pi\sqrt{\frac{m}{k}}$$

The restoring force is the force applied by the springs. For example, when the trolley is displaced to the left of the equilibrium position, there is a greater tension in the right-hand spring, tending to decelerate the trolley (if it is moving away from the equilibrium position) or accelerate it (if moving towards the equilibrium position).

> Stiffness k = force per metre of extension, i.e. how many newtons are required to stretch the spring 1 metre.

? Quick check questions

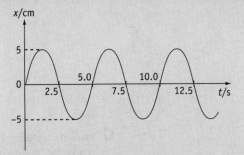

x/cm

1 For the oscillation represented by the graph, what are the values of: amplitude, period, frequency?

2 The swings of a pendulum are timed. It completes 20 swings in 17.4 s. What are its period and frequency?

3 A mass is vibrating on the end of a spring. Its acceleration a (in m s^{-2}) is related to its displacement x (in m) from a fixed point by $a = -(40\pi)^2 x$. What is its frequency? What is the period of its oscillation?

More about SHM

We can think of oscillations that are simple harmonic as being 'pure' oscillations. They give an x–t graph that is a cosine curve, if time is counted starting from the end point of the oscillation.

SHM graphs

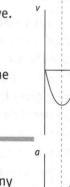

The velocity–time graph is the gradient of the displacement–time graph. (See the upper two graphs alongside.)

- At the start of the x–t graph, the gradient is zero, so the velocity is zero.
- When the x–t graph first crosses the t-axis, its gradient is steep and negative. The velocity is negative and has its maximum magnitude.

The a–t graph is the gradient of the v–t graph. It has troughs where the x–t graph has peaks. (Recall that the acceleration is in the opposite direction to the displacement.)

SHM equations

Displacement

If the oscillation starts ($t = 0$) at the endpoint ($x = A$), the displacement x at any time t after the start can be calculated using the equation

$$x = A \cos 2\pi f t$$

Take care! When using this equation, ensure that your calculator is working in radians, not degrees!

▶▶ *More about radians on page 28.*

✓ *Quick check 1*

Velocity

To find the velocity at any displacement x, use the equation

$$v = \pm(2\pi f) \sqrt{A^2 - x^2}$$

The velocity is a maximum when $x = 0$:

$$v_{max} = \pm(2\pi f) \sqrt{A^2 - 0^2}$$

So

$$v_{max} = \pm(2\pi f)A$$

At the endpoints, $x = A$, so $v = 0$.

Acceleration

The acceleration graph has the same shape as the displacement graph, but acceleration is negative when displacement is positive, and acceleration is positive when displacement is negative. Thus acceleration is directly proportional to minus displacement:

$$a = -constant \times x$$
$$a = -(2\pi f)^2 x$$

▶▶ *See also pages 6–7.*

> ◖ Remember velocity is a vector, so the sign must be taken into account.

✓ *Quick check 2, 3*

Back and forth

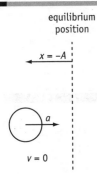

equilibrium
position

$x = -A$

a

$v = 0$

at extreme left

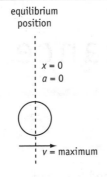

equilibrium
position

$x = 0$
$a = 0$

v = maximum

in centre

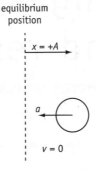

equilibrium
position

$x = +A$

a

$v = 0$

at extreme right

Here, the restoring force F has its greatest value. The mass is instantaneously at rest.

displacement $x = -A$

velocity $v = 0$

acceleration a = maximum
$= (2\pi f)^2 A$

At the midpoint, the mass is moving fastest, although there is no force on it. It is in equilibrium ($F = 0$).

displacement $x = 0$

velocity v = maximum
$= (2\pi f)A$

acceleration $a = 0$

Here, the mass's velocity is again zero, but the restoring force again has its maximum value.

displacement $x = +A$

velocity $v = 0$

acceleration a = maximum
$= -(2\pi f)^2 A$

The mass speeds up as it approaches the midpoint. As soon as it passes through the midpoint, it starts to decelerate.

✓ Quick check 4, 5

? Quick check questions

1

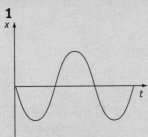

The graph shows one oscillation for a vibrating mass. Copy the graph, and beneath it sketch the corresponding velocity–time and acceleration–time graphs.

2 A mass oscillates such that its displacement x in mm is represented by the equation

$$x = 40 \cos (0.6t)$$

Determine the values of the amplitude and frequency of this motion. What is the value of x when $t = 5$ s?

3 Write an equation relating displacement x and time t for oscillations of amplitude 0.2 m and frequency 0.5 Hz, for a mass whose initial displacement is +0.2 m. Calculate the displacement of the mass when $t = 0.3$ s.

4 Calculate the maximum speed of the mass in Question 2.

5 A pendulum swings from side to side. At what point in its oscillation is its speed greatest? At what point is its acceleration greatest?

Energy changes, damping and resonance

Energy changes

For a pendulum, the energy of the oscillating mass is transformed back and forth between kinetic and potential forms.

- Midpoint: maximum velocity, therefore maximum E_K and zero E_P
- Endpoints: zero velocity, therefore zero E_K and maximum E_P
- The total energy ($E_K + E_P$) is constant.

For a mass oscillating vertically on a spring, the potential energy is partly gravitational potential energy and partly elastic strain energy. At all times the total energy (potential + kinetic) is constant. This is true for all freely oscillating systems.

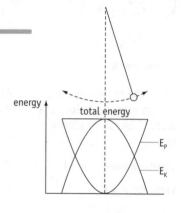

✓ *Quick check 1*

Damping

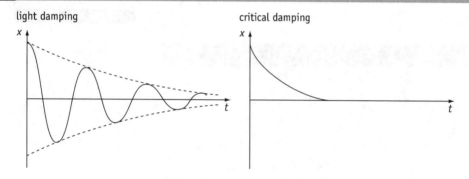

If an oscillating mass loses no energy, it will oscillate for ever with the same amplitude. However, if it loses energy, we say the oscillations are **damped**. Their amplitude decreases.

- Light damping: the amplitude decreases gradually as the mass oscillates.
- Critical damping: the damping is heavy enough for the displacement just to decrease to zero (the equilibrium position) without oscillation. With a little less damping, the mass overshoots the equilibrium position.

Damping is caused by frictional forces, e.g. drag of the air, or viscous drag in oil. If a sheet of card is stuck onto the oscillating mass on the end of a vertical spring, air resistance will provide damping. If the mass is immersed in water or oil, the damping is increased and its amplitude decreases more sharply.

A car suspension system is usually critically damped, so that the passengers do not bounce up and down each time the car passes over a bump in the road.

The time for each full oscillation remains the same despite the decrease in amplitude from one oscillation to the next.

✓ *Quick check 2*

Resonance

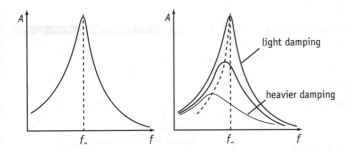

It may be possible to force a mass to oscillate at any frequency by applying a periodic force. This is called a **forced oscillation** or forced vibration. If the forcing frequency matches the natural frequency f_0 of free oscillations, the amplitude increases to a large value. This is **resonance**.

The graph shows that:

- at frequencies slightly above and below resonance, the amplitude is less;
- damping reduces the amplitude at resonance, and tends to shift the resonant frequency slightly.

Some examples of resonance are as follows:

- Pushing a child on a swing – maximum amplitude is reached when the pushing frequency equals the natural frequency.
- Tuning a radio – the resonant frequency of the tuning circuit is adjusted to equal the frequency of the signal.
- In pipe instruments a column of air is forced to vibrate; if the forcing frequency equals the natural frequency of the column, a loud sound is heard.
- Rotating machinery – in a washing machine an out-of-balance drum may cause violent vibrations at certain speeds.

✓ *Quick check 2, 3*

❓ Quick check questions

1 Look at the energy graph opposite. When the oscillating mass is half-way between the midpoint and the endpoint of its oscillation, which is greater, its E_K or its E_P?

2 Look at the resonance graph above. What happens to the sharpness of the resonance curve as damping increases?

3 Give two examples where resonance is useful and two where resonance is a nuisance or potentially damaging.

Representing waves

We see waves on the surface of water. They travel across the surface of the water, transferring energy; the molecules of the water move up and down. A wave is a periodic disturbance of the water.

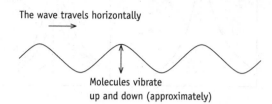

The wave travels horizontally

Molecules vibrate
up and down (approximately)

The top diagram represents the wave as an idealised **sine wave**. This idea can be used as a model for other phenomena:

- **Sound waves** travel through air (or any other medium). The particles of the medium vibrate back and forth as the wave travels along, as shown in the lower diagram.

- **Light** (and other **electromagnetic waves**) do not require a medium. They are a periodic variation of an electric field and a magnetic field. These fields vary at right angles to one another and to the direction of travel of the wave.

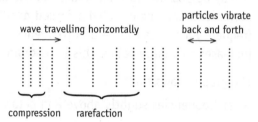

wave travelling horizontally

particles vibrate
back and forth

compression   rarefaction

Transverse and longitudinal waves

There are two types of wave – *transverse* and *longitudinal*.

Transverse waves can be made to travel along a stretched rope, by moving one end up and down (or from side to side). Both types of wave can be demonstrated using a long spring; for longitudinal waves, the end of the spring must be pushed back and forth. However, it is simplest to represent waves, transverse or longitudinal, as sine waves.

transverse wave

Vibrations are perpendicular to direction of travel. Water waves and electromagnetic waves are examples of transverse waves.

longitudinal wave

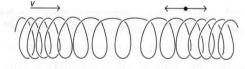

Vibrations are back-and-forth, along direction of travel. Sound waves are longitudinal.

✓ *Quick check 1, 2*

❶ Although we may represent a sound wave using a sine curve, the particles move back-and-forth, not up-and-down.

Polarisation

Light (and other transverse waves) can be **polarised**. In unpolarised light, the electric and magnetic fields vibrate in all directions perpendicular to the direction of travel. After passing through a sheet of Polaroid, each vibrates in only one direction or plane. The light is said to be **plane polarised**.

A second sheet of Polaroid will let through nearly all the light if its plane of polarisation is lined up with that of the first sheet. If it is 'crossed' (at 90°) with the first, all the plane polarised vibrations will be absorbed and no light will pass through.

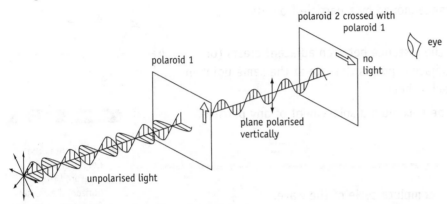

In the diagram, the arrow on the Polaroid indicates the direction of polarisation of the light it lets through.

Reflected light is partially plane polarised. Light reflected from a pond or the sea is mainly horizontally polarised. Polaroid sunglasses let through vibrations only in a vertical plane, so they cut out the reflected light, reducing glare.

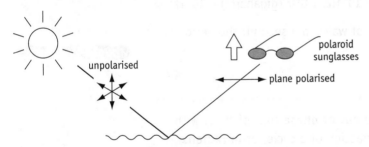

Only transverse waves can be polarised. If a wave can be polarised, it *must* be transverse – that's how we know electromagnetic waves are transverse.

✓ *Quick check 3*

? *Quick check questions*

1 Classify as transverse or longitudinal: light, sound, water, infrared waves.
2 A guitarist plucks a string. A wave travels along the string. Is this longitudinal or transverse?
3 Which of these can be polarised: light waves; microwaves; sound waves?

Wave quantities

Several quantities are needed to fully describe a wave: **amplitude**, **wavelength**, **frequency**, **phase**. Learn how they are related; take care not to confuse them.

Wavelength and amplitude

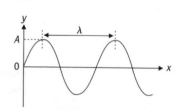

- The **displacement y** is the distance moved by a particle from its undisturbed position.
- The **wavelength** λ of a wave is the distance between adjacent crests (or troughs), or between any two adjacent points that are at the same point in the cycle (i.e. **in phase** with each other).
- The **amplitude A** of a wave is the maximum displacement of any particle.

✓ **Quick check 1**

Period and frequency

▶ Amplitude is the height of a crest measured from the horizontal axis, not from crest to trough.

- The **period T** is the time for one complete cycle of the wave.
- This is related to the wave's **frequency f**: $T = \dfrac{1}{f}$ (or $f = \dfrac{1}{T}$).

- The frequency f is the number of cycles of the wave per second.
- Frequency is measured in **hertz** (**Hz**).
- 1 kHz (kilohertz) = 10^3 Hz, 1 MHz (megahertz) = 10^6 Hz, 1 GHz (gigahertz) = 10^9 Hz.

Think of it like this: the frequency is the number of waves per second; the period is the number of seconds per wave.

▶ Take care! The horizontal axis of this graph is *time*, not distance.

✓ **Quick check 2**

Phase difference

Two waves may have the same wavelength but be **out of phase** (out of step) with one another. Phase difference is expressed as a fraction of a cycle, or in **radians** (rad) or **degrees** (°).

▶▶ *More about radians on page 28.*

- 1 cycle = 1 complete wave = 2π rad = 360°

two waves in phase

- $\dfrac{1}{2}$ cycle = π rad = 180°

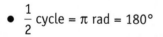
phase difference = ½ cycle

- $\dfrac{1}{4}$ cycle = $\dfrac{\pi}{2}$ rad = 90°

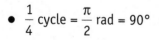
phase difference = ¼ cycle

✓ **Quick check 3**

Wave speed, frequency and wavelength

Waves are one way in which energy is transferred from place to place. How quickly they do this depends on their speed, which may be anything up to c, the speed of light in free space, 3×10^8 m s^{-1}.

The waves we have considered so far are described as **progressive waves**. They travel through a medium or through space. The **speed v** of the wave tells us how fast it moves. The speed is the distance travelled per second by a crest.

Speed v is related to frequency f and wavelength λ by

> **speed = frequency × wavelength $v = f\lambda$**

If a 'train' of f waves, each of length λ, passes a point in 1 s, the total length of the train is $f\lambda$. This is the length of the waves passing the point per second, i.e. the speed of the wave.

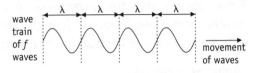

Worked examples

1 An observer, standing at the end of a pier, sees one wave passing by every 8 s. The distance between adjacent peaks is 12 m. Calculate the speed of the waves.
Step 1 Calculate the frequency of the waves.
$$f = 1/8 \text{ s} = 0.125 \text{ Hz}$$
Step 2 Note down the wavelength of the waves.
$$\lambda = 12 \text{ m}$$
Step 3 Calculate the wave speed.
$$\text{speed } v = f\lambda = 0.125 \text{ Hz} \times 12 \text{ m} = 1.5 \text{ m s}^{-1}$$

2 Calculate the wavelength of an electromagnetic wave (speed $= 3 \times 10^8$ m s^{-1}) of frequency 100 GHz.
Step 1 Write down quantities; convert to scientific notation (powers of 10).
$$v = 3 \times 10^8 \text{ m s}^{-1}, f = 100 \text{ GHz} = 100 \times 10^9 \text{ Hz}, \lambda = ?$$
Step 2 Rearrange the equation, substitute values and solve.
$$\lambda = v/f = \frac{3 \times 10^8 \text{ m s}^{-1}}{100 \times 10^9 \text{ Hz}} = 3 \times 10^{-3} \text{ m}$$

> ◖ It is simplest to change units such as GHz to powers of 10; then enter them into your calculator in this form. You could give this answer as $\lambda = 3$ mm.

> ✓ *Quick check 4, 5*

❓ *Quick check questions*

1 What quantities are represented by p and q in the diagram? What are their values?

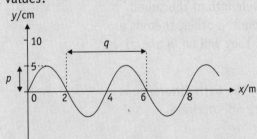

2 Calculate the period for waves of the following frequencies: 2.0 Hz, 2.0 kHz, 0.5 MHz.

3 On the same axes, sketch two waves with a phase difference of π radians; one wave has twice the amplitude of the other.

4 Calculate the speed of ripples whose wavelength is 3.0 mm and whose frequency is 15 Hz.

5 Calculate the frequency of a sound wave if its wavelength in air is 11 mm. (Speed of sound in air $= 330$ m s^{-1}.)

Interference and diffraction

What happens when two waves cross? Two snooker balls would bounce off one another, but waves behave differently. They show behaviour known as **interference**. Interference may be **destructive** or **constructive**.

Destructive interference

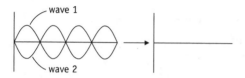

wave 1

wave 2

Constructive interference

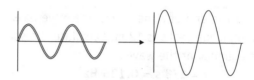

| two waves arriving out of phase (out of step) | they cancel each other out | two waves arriving in phase (in step) | resultant is wave of twice the amplitude |

✓ **Quick check 1**

Interference of sound

Walking around in the space beyond the two loudspeakers, you can hear points where the sound is loud, and points where it is much softer. These loud and soft points have a regular pattern.

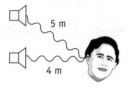

5 m

4 m

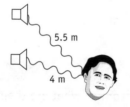

5.5 m

4 m

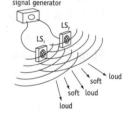

signal generator

LS$_2$

LS$_1$

loud
soft
soft loud
loud

Your ear receives waves from both speakers. Suppose the wavelength of the sound waves is 1 m. If your ear is 4 m from one speaker and 5 m from the other, there is a **path difference** of 1 m (one wavelength) for the two waves. They will be *in phase*; they will interfere constructively and you hear a loud sound.

If your ear is 4 m from one speaker and 5.5 m from the other, the path difference is 1.5 m (1½ wavelengths). The waves will be *out of phase*; they will interfere destructively and you hear no sound (or a very faint sound).

- For constructive interference, path difference = $n\lambda$, where n is any whole number: 1, 2, 3, ..., etc.

- For destructive interference, path difference = $(n + \frac{1}{2})\lambda$.

Interference of other waves

The same effect can be shown for:

- *ripples* – use two dippers attached to a vibrating bar in a ripple tank;

- *microwaves* – direct the microwaves through two gaps in a metal plate;

- *light* – the 'Young's double-slit' experiment – *see page 18*.

Diffraction

When ripples pass through a gap, they spread out into the space beyond. The effect, which is known as **diffraction**, is greatest when the width x of the gap is similar to the wavelength λ of the ripples. The same thing happens with light waves – light passing through a single narrow slit will spread out.

✓ *Quick check 2*

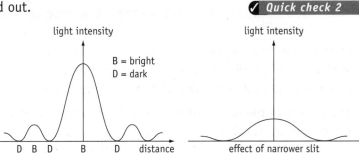

width of gap = x

$\lambda \ll x$ $\lambda < x$ $\lambda \simeq x$

light intensity

B = bright
D = dark

D B D   B   D   distance

light intensity

effect of narrower slit

Explaining diffraction

When light from a laser is shone through a single slit, a **diffraction pattern** of light and dark interference bands (called '*fringes*') is seen on the screen. We picture waves spreading out from all points in the slit. Each point on the screen receives waves from each point in the slit. These waves interfere.

- Where all the interfering waves cancel each other out, we see a dark fringe (*destructive* interference).

- Where all the interfering waves add up, we see a bright fringe (*constructive* interference).

The centre of the fringe pattern is brightest, with the other bright fringes getting dimmer as you go further from the centre of the pattern.

✓ *Quick check 3*

Coherent sources

To observe an interference pattern where two sets of waves overlap, they must be **coherent**. This means they must have the same wavelength and frequency; also, the phase difference between them must be constant.

Light from a lamp is not usually coherent. It is emitted as photons, and they do not keep in step with one another. Laser light is coherent; its photons remain in step between source and screen.

✓ *Quick check 4*

? *Quick check questions*

1. Two waves are in phase and one has twice the amplitude of the other. What will be observed if these two waves interfere?

2. Draw a ripple diagram (like those at the top of this page) to show ripples of wavelength λ being diffracted by a gap of width 2λ. Draw a second diagram to show what happens if ripples of wavelength 2λ pass through this gap.

3. A narrow beam of light from a laser is shone onto a single narrow slit, and a diffraction pattern is formed on a screen. Describe the effect on the pattern of gradually reducing the width of the slit.

4. Two dippers are used to produce an interference pattern in a ripple tank. Are they a pair of coherent sources?

Young's double-slit experiment

Light shows *interference*. To produce two waves, light is shone through a pair of parallel slits. Where the light falls on a screen beyond the slits, light and dark interference 'fringes' are seen.

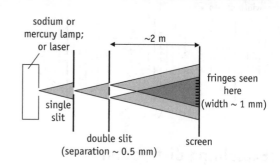

- The light from the slits must be *coherent*. The light leaving the double slit is coherent if the double slit is placed in front of an illuminated single slit. Alternatively, a laser can be shone directly on the double slit.

- As light passes through each slit, it spreads out into the space beyond. This is *diffraction* – see page 17.

- The fringe separation can be measured using a travelling microscope. If a laser is used, the fringe separation can be measured fairly accurately by marking the fringes on graph paper stuck on a screen a few metres away.

- Increasing the slit–screen distance makes the fringes wider but dimmer.

WARNING: You must not look into the laser – you should wear laser spectacles or laser goggles.

▶ Remember that laser light is coherent – see page 17.

✓ *Quick check 1*

Explaining the interference fringes

Each point on the screen receives light waves from both slits (S_1 and S_2).

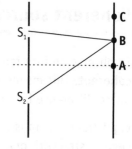

- **A** is the point on the screen directly opposite the point midway between the two slits. If waves leave the two slits in phase with one another, they will arrive at point **A** in phase. They will interfere constructively and a bright fringe will be seen. Path difference = 0.

- **B** is the centre of the first dark fringe. A wave from S_1 has a shorter distance to travel than a wave from S_2. The two waves arrive out of phase and interfere destructively. Path difference = $S_2\mathbf{B} - S_1\mathbf{B} = \dfrac{\lambda}{2}$.

- **C** is the centre of the next bright fringe. The two waves arrive in phase, but one has travelled further than the other. Path difference = λ.

Therefore:

- A bright fringe is seen where the two waves arrive in phase; path difference = $n\lambda$ (n = 0, 1, 2, 3, ..., etc.).

- A dark fringe is seen where they arrive out of phase; path difference = $(n + \frac{1}{2})\lambda$.

- In-between positions have in-between path differences that give rise to intermediate brightnesses.

✓ *Quick check 2*

Measuring the wavelength of light

The Young's slits experiment provides a method for determining λ, which is related to the screen distance D, slit separation s and fringe width w by:

$$\lambda = \frac{ws}{D}$$

Note that, for white light, this can give only an average value of λ since many wavelengths are present. Laser light is monochromatic (a single wavelength), so the fringes are clearer and a more accurate value of λ can be found.

> You may find it easier to remember the formula as $\lambda D = ws$:
> largest quantity (D) times smallest (λ) equals other two multiplied

✓ Quick check 3

Worked example

Laser light of wavelength 648 nm falls on a pair of slits separated by 1.5 mm. What will be the separation of the interference fringes seen on a screen 4.5 m from the slits?

Step 1 Write down what you know, and what you want to know:

$$\lambda = 648 \text{ nm}, s = 1.5 \text{ mm}, D = 4.5 \text{ m}, w = ?$$

Step 2 Rearrange the equation, substitute values and solve:

$$w = \frac{\lambda D}{s} = \frac{648 \times 10^{-9} \text{ m} \times 4.5 \text{ m}}{1.5 \times 10^{-3} \text{ m}} = 1.9 \times 10^{-3} \text{ m}$$

So the fringe width seen on the screen will be 1.9 mm.

✓ Quick check 4

❓ Quick check questions

1 Give the symbol and approximate size for each of the following in the Young's slits experiment: slit–screen distance; slit separation; fringe separation; wavelength of light.

2 What can you say about the path difference between two waves that show destructive interference?

3 If the slit separation s is doubled, how will the fringe width w be changed?

4 White light is directed onto a pair of slits separated by 1.0 mm. Interference fringes are observed on a screen at a distance of 1.8 m. Five fringes have a width of 5.0 mm. Estimate the wavelength of the light. Why is your answer an estimate?

Superposition and stationary waves

When two or more waves cross at a point, the result is found by the **principle of superposition**. At any instant, the resultant displacement is simply the sum of the displacements of the individual waves. Constructive and destructive interference are obvious examples of this idea. It also explains the formation of **stationary waves**.

Stationary waves on a stretched string

The vibrator sends waves along the string. They are reflected at each end. The outgoing and reflected waves then interfere. At certain frequencies, a **stationary wave** (or **standing wave**) pattern of loops is formed.

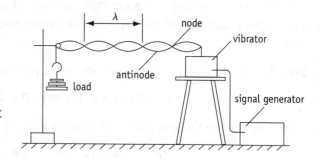

- At certain points – **nodes** – the two waves interfere destructively. There is no vibration. There are nodes at the ends of the string.

- Half-way between the nodes are **antinodes**. The string vibrates with a large amplitude.

- Changing the frequency slightly causes the stationary wave to disappear. Changing the length, tension or thickness of the string causes the stationary waves to appear at different frequencies.

- The wavelength of the wave is *twice* the distance from one node to the next.

✓ *Quick check 1*

Conditions for a stationary wave

Two identical but oppositely travelling waves interfere with each other to form a stationary wave. Often, one wave is a reflection of the other. For example, when microwaves are reflected by a metal plate, a stationary wave pattern is formed.

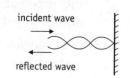

Using the principle of superposition

✓ *Quick check 2*

The diagrams show the two waves that make a stationary wave. They are shown at three instants in time. You can see that the waves are progressive waves, travelling in opposite directions.

Below these are the resultant waves. These are worked out by adding the displacements of the two progressive waves.

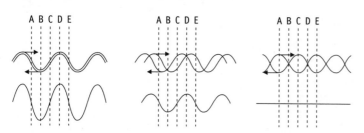

- Points A, C and E are nodes; the two waves always cancel here.
- Points B and D are antinodes; the displacement here varies up and down.

✓ *Quick check 3*

Between one node and the next all particles are in phase, but particles in adjacent 'loops' are 180° (or π rad) out of phase.

- P is in phase with Q.
- R is 180° out of phase with both P and Q.

Air columns

When the frequency of the loudspeaker is changed, a point is reached where the note becomes much louder. Sound waves are reflected by the water and a stationary wave has formed in the air column inside the cylinder. There is a node at the foot of the air column and an antinode at the top.

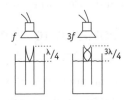

At the lowest frequency at which this occurs, the length of the air column is one quarter of the wavelength of the sound. A stationary wave is formed again at three times this frequency, with three-quarters of a wave fitting in the column.

✓ *Quick check 4*

Microwaves

Direct microwaves at a vertical metal plate. Reflected waves interfere with incoming waves to form a stationary wave pattern. Detect nodes (zero intensity) and antinodes (high intensity) between source and plate.

> ▶ Note that the wave is represented by showing the maximum displacement of air particles with distance along the tube. Remember that it is actually a longitudinal stationary wave.

❓ *Quick check questions*

1 A string of length 1.2 m is stretched and vibrated so that a stationary wave consisting of two loops is formed. Sketch this, and calculate the wavelength of the waves on the string.

2 Microwaves are directed at a sheet of steel. A detector is used to investigate the intensity of the waves between the source and the plate. A pattern of high and low intensity regions is found; the separation of adjacent high intensity regions is 15 mm. What is the wavelength of the microwaves?

3 Explain why there is a node at point C in the diagram at the foot of the opposite page.

4 In a vibrating air column experiment, the air column is 0.20 m long. The lowest frequency that produces a stationary wave is 400 Hz. Calculate the wavelength and speed of the sound waves.

The diffraction grating

A **diffraction grating** is a set of parallel slits made by forming very thin grooves ('lines') in glass or transparent plastic film.

When a ray of laser light is shone through a slit and then through a diffraction grating at 90°, a series of widely spaced, sharp bright bands are formed on a screen.

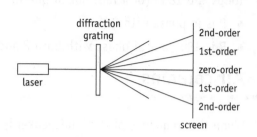

Explaining the pattern

If the angle θ in the diagram is such that a wave from a point B in one slit is exactly in phase with a wave from a corresponding point A in the adjacent slit, the path difference AC must be:

- λ for the first bright band (called the *first-order principal maximum*),
- 2λ for the second bright band (the *second-order principal maximum*),
- 3λ for the third bright band, ...,
- $n\lambda$ for the nth bright band.

Zooming in on triangle ABC,

$$\sin \theta = \frac{AC}{AB} = \frac{AC}{d} = \frac{n\lambda}{d}$$

Rearranging,

$$n\lambda = d \sin \theta$$

- The bands become further apart if the line spacing decreases (i.e. if the number of lines per mm increases).
- $\lambda_{red} > \lambda_{violet}$, so θ for red light is greater than for violet light.
- If white light is used, the central band (the *'zero-order maximum'*) is white, but those on each side of the central spot are coloured violet on the inside, and red on the outside.

> ▶ If the first-order angle is θ, don't be tempted to think the second-order angle is 2θ. You must use the formula.

✓ *Quick check 1*

Worked example

Light from a sodium vapour lamp is shone through a slit and then through a diffraction grating at 90° to the ray of light. The grating has 300 lines per mm. The first-order maximum is found to occur at an angle of 10.2°.

What is the wavelength of the light? How many bright bands would appear on each side of the central maximum?

Step 1 Write down what you know, and what you want to know:

$$n = 1 \text{ (first order)}, \theta = 10.2°$$

$$d = \frac{1}{\text{lines per metre}} = \frac{1}{300000} = 3.33 \times 10^{-6} \text{ m}$$

Step 2 Substitute values for n, θ and d in the formula $n\lambda = d\sin\theta$:

$$1 \times \lambda = 3.33 \times 10^{-6} \text{ m} \times \sin 10.2°$$

$$\lambda = 5.90 \times 10^{-7} \text{ m or } 590 \text{ nm}$$

Step 3 There is a limit to n since $\sin\theta$ cannot be greater than 1. Put $\sin\theta = 1$ in $n\lambda = d\sin\theta$ and rearrange:

$$n = \frac{d}{\lambda} = \frac{3.33 \times 10^{-6} \text{ m}}{5.90 \times 10^{-7} \text{ m}} = 5.6$$

However, n must be a whole number, so five bright bands would be seen either side of the central maximum, i.e. a total of 11 bright bands in all.

✓ *Quick check 2, 3*

Applications

Use of a diffraction grating:

- provides an accurate method for measuring the wavelength of light;
- can separate wavelengths that are very close together;
- can identify very small quantities of materials (since different elements give different spectra);
- enables scientists to analyse the light from stars, nebulae and interstellar gas and hence determine their make-up.

Quick check questions

1 A narrow beam of light of wavelength 450 nm is shone at 90° onto a diffraction grating that has 200 lines per mm. Find the angles of the first and second maxima.

2 For the arrangement described in Question 1, how many bright bands (maxima) are produced in total?

3 A diffraction grating is illuminated with a narrow beam of monochromatic light normal to its surface. Light passing through the grating falls on a screen about a metre away. State the effect on the bright bands seen on the screen when

  a the wavelength of the light is increased;

  b the diffraction grating is replaced by one with half the number of slits per mm;

  c the diffraction grating is replaced by one with the same number of slits per mm, but with the width of each slit halved.

Capacitors

Capacitors are components used in circuits to store electric charge. They usually consist of two parallel metal plates, separated by a thin layer of insulating material.

Stored charge

When a capacitor is connected to a source of voltage (p.d.), electrons flow from the negative end of the supply to one plate, which gains negative charge $-Q$, and electrons are repelled from the other plate, which is left with positive charge $+Q$. The capacitor is said to store Q coulombs of charge.

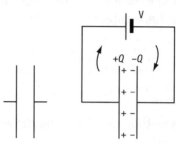 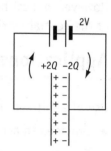

Increasing the voltage pushes more charge onto the capacitor. The greater the voltage V and the greater the capacitance C of the capacitor, the more charge Q it stores. This is represented by the equation

> **charge stored = capacitance × p.d. $Q = CV$**

Definitions

The equation $Q = CV$ can be rearranged to define capacitance:

$$C = \frac{Q}{V}$$

The capacitance of a capacitor is the charge stored for each volt of potential difference across it.

Units   Capacitance is measured in **farads** (F). One farad is one coulomb per volt. Most practical capacitors have values measured in smaller units:

- $1\ \mu F = 1$ microfarad $= 10^{-6}$ F
- $1\ pF = 1$ picofarad $= 10^{-12}$ F

> ❗ Don't confuse C (for coulomb, the *unit* of charge Q) with C, the *symbol* for capacitance.

> ✓ *Quick check 1*

Storing energy

When a capacitor is charged up, work is done by the p.d. that pushes the charge onto the plates. This means that a charged capacitor is a *store of energy*.

Since work done = energy transferred = charge × voltage, it follows that the energy E stored by a charged capacitor is the triangular area under the Q–V graph. Using the formula for the area of a triangle ($\frac{1}{2}$ × base × height):

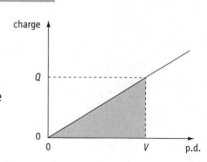

$$\text{energy stored} = \tfrac{1}{2} \times \text{charge} \times \text{p.d.} \quad \text{or} \quad E = \tfrac{1}{2} QV$$

Substituting $Q = CV$ gives $E = \dfrac{1}{2}CV^2$, and substituting $V = \dfrac{Q}{C}$ gives $E = \dfrac{1}{2}\dfrac{Q^2}{C}$.

Hence there are three forms of the equation, the first being the fundamental one:

$$E = \frac{1}{2}QV = \frac{1}{2}CV^2 = \frac{1}{2}\frac{Q^2}{C}$$

✓ **Quick check 2**

Charging a capacitor

A capacitor connected directly to a battery will charge up almost instantaneously. If a resistor of resistance R is placed in series with the capacitor, charging takes longer.

During charging, charge Q and voltage V follow the same pattern.

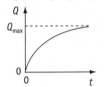

charge stored increases rapidly at first, then more slowly

Q_{max} = supply p.d. × C

more charge stored means more p.d. across capacitor

max V = supply p.d.

p.d. across capacitor opposes supply p.d., so as capacitor p.d. gets bigger, current drops

$$I_0 = \frac{\text{supply p.d.}}{R}$$

Time constant CR

The time taken for the capacitor to charge depends on C and R. The quantity CR is called the **time constant** of the circuit: symbol τ (Greek tau); unit seconds (s).

$$\text{time constant } \tau = CR$$

The time constant is the time for the charge (or voltage) to *rise* to 63% (0.63) of its *final* steady value.

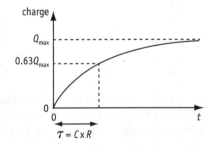

✓ **Quick check 3**

? ## Quick check questions

1 A capacitor stores 40 µC of charge when connected to a 5.0 V supply. What is its capacitance? How much charge will it store when connected to a 20 V supply?

2 A capacitor stores 10 mJ of energy when connected to a 100 V supply. What is its capacitance? How much energy will it store when connected to a 200 V supply?

3 Which has the greater time constant, a circuit with a 20 µF capacitor and a 5.0 MΩ resistor, or a circuit with a 1000 µF capacitor and a 100 kΩ resistor?

Discharging a capacitor

When a charged capacitor is disconnected from the supply used to charge it up, it can be discharged by connecting it across a resistor. The greater the resistance, the more slowly the capacitor will discharge.

Discharge investigation

- Close switch S, adjust power supply voltage to give $I = 100$ µA.

- Open S and start the data logger (set to sample every second). Stop logging when the current is nearly zero.

- Using the logged values, produce a graph of voltage against time.

- Try altering resistance R and capacitance C (e.g. to 220 µF, which means you can see the effect of approximately halving the capacitance).

- If you want the current curve, start recording current manually when $I = 100$ µA (this gives an easy start for your current graph). Record current every 10 s.

During discharge, charge Q, p.d. V and current I all follow the same pattern, an **exponential decay curve**. This curve is always getting closer to zero, without (theoretically) ever reaching it.

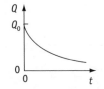

Charge stored decreases rapidly at first, then more and more slowly

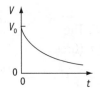

Less charge stored means less p.d. across capacitor, so p.d. follows same pattern

As p.d. decreases, current through resistor must also decrease

✓ **Quick check 1**

Discharge equations

$Q = Q_0 e^{-t/CR}$	$V = V_0 e^{-t/CR}$	$I = I_0 e^{-t/CR}$
Q_0 = initial charge (i.e. when $t = 0$)	V_0 = initial p.d.	I_0 = initial current
$Q_0 = CV_0$	$V_0 = I_0 R$	$I_0 = \dfrac{V_0}{R}$

These equations can be used to find values of Q, V and I at any time during the discharge. Make sure you know how to use the e^x function on your calculator – see the worked example.

In the examination, you are likely to be asked to use only the equation for charge $Q = Q_0 e^{-t/CR}$, but you will also need to know the relationships in the last line giving the starting charge, starting voltage and starting current.

Worked example

A 10 μF capacitor is charged to 20 V, then discharged through a 50 kΩ resistor. Calculate the initial charge on the capacitor and the charge on it after 2.0 s.

Step 1 Calculate the initial charge, Q_0:

$$Q_0 = V_0 C = 20 \text{ V} \times (10 \times 10^{-6} \text{ F}) = 200 \text{ μC}$$

Step 2 Using your calculator, calculate the quantity $-t/CR$ that appears in the exponential function:

$$\frac{-t}{CR} = \frac{-2.0}{10 \times 10^{-6} \times 50 \times 10^{3}} = -4.0$$

> This quantity has no units, so there is no need to include them.

Step 3 Use your calculator's e^x key, then multiply by Q_0:

$$Q = Q_0 e^{-t/CR} = 200 \text{ μC} \times e^{-4} = 3.7 \text{ μC}$$

With practice, you can merge steps 2 and 3.

✓ *Quick check 2, 3*

Time constant *CR*

The time constant $\tau = CR$ was introduced in the section on charging a capacitor, on page 25. For discharging, it is defined similarly, as the time for the charge (or p.d., or current) to *fall* to about 37% (0.37) of its *initial* value (to be exact, $\frac{1}{e}$).

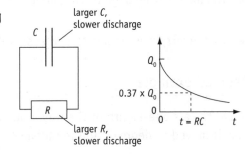

larger *C*, slower discharge

larger *R*, slower discharge

The graphs of the variation of Q and V with time for *charging* a capacitor are the same shape as the *discharging* curves but are *inverted* (upside-down). The current curve is the same for both charging and discharging. (See pages 25 and 26.)

✓ *Quick check 4*

❓ Quick check questions

1   A capacitor is charged and discharged through a resistor. It is then charged again to the same p.d., and discharged through a resistor of twice the resistance. Which of the two graphs shown represents the second discharge? Give a reason to support your answer.

2   A 20 pF capacitor is charged to 100 V. Calculate the charge on the capacitor. The capacitor is then discharged through a 500 MΩ resistor. What will be the charge on the capacitor 0.015 s after discharging starts?

3   A 12 V battery is used to charge a 1000 μF capacitor, which is then discharged through a 50 kΩ resistor. Calculate the initial current that flows, and the current after 50 s.

4   Calculate the time constant for the capacitor–resistor combination of Question 2.

> For the current after 50 s, first find the time constant.

Describing circular motion

Many objects move along paths that are circular (or nearly circular) – a stone whirled around on the end of a piece of string, the Earth in its orbit around the Sun, a car along a curved stretch of road, an aircraft changing direction, an electron orbiting the nucleus of an atom. Since an object moving along a curved path is not moving in a straight line, it is an example of a moving object that is not in equilibrium.

Angular displacement; angles in radians

start

As an object moves along a circular path, it can be useful to state its position in terms of the angle θ through which it has moved relative to its starting position. This is called its **angular displacement** and is often given in **radians**, rather than degrees. The abbreviation for radians is **rad.**

- To convert from degrees to radians: multiply by $\dfrac{\pi}{180}$.

- To convert from radians to degrees: multiply by $\dfrac{180}{\pi}$.

$\theta = 1$ rad

Worked example

A car travels one-eighth of the way around a circular track. Through what angle θ has it moved in degrees, and in radians?

Step 1 Since a full circle is 360°, we can calculate the angle in degrees:

$$\theta = \frac{360°}{8} = 45°$$

Step 2 Convert to radians:

$$\theta = 45° \times \frac{\pi}{180} \text{ rad} = \frac{\pi}{4} \text{ rad} = 0.79 \text{ rad}$$

2π rad = 360°

π rad = 180°

$\dfrac{\pi}{2}$ rad = 90°

✓ *Quick check 1, 2*

Speed around a circular path

To calculate the speed of an object moving in a circular path, we need to know a distance and a time. For example:

$$\text{speed} = \frac{\text{circumference of circle}}{\text{time to complete one circuit}}$$

Since the circumference of a circle of radius r is $2\pi r$, if the time to complete one circuit is t we have

$$v = \frac{2\pi r}{t}$$

✓ *Quick check 3*

Angular speed

The **angular speed** is the angle in radians swept out by the radius every second. It has the symbol ω (omega) and the unit rad s^{-1}. A spoke of a wheel will sweep out an angle of 2π radians every time the wheel rotates.

Worked example

Calculate the angular speed of a food processor blade rotating at 500 rev min^{-1}.

Step 1 Change rev min^{-1} to rev s^{-1}:

$$500 \text{ rev min}^{-1} = \frac{500}{60} \text{ rev s}^{-1} = 8.33 \text{ rev s}^{-1}$$

Step 2 The blade sweeps out 2π rad every revolution, so the angular speed is

$$\omega = 8.33 \times 2\pi = 52.3 \text{ rad s}^{-1}$$

Speed, angular speed and frequency

The number of revolutions per second is sometimes called the frequency, f. You can see from the above example that frequency $\times 2\pi$ gives the angular speed:

$$\omega = 2\pi f$$

The speed v (in m s^{-1}) of an object moving in a circle of radius r is related to the angular speed ω (in rad s^{-1}) of the rotating radius by

$$v = r\omega$$

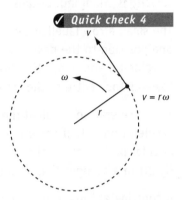

✓ *Quick check 4*

✓ *Quick check 5*

Quick check questions

1 Convert the following angles in degrees to radians: 360°; 180°; 90°; 60°; 45°.

2 Convert the following angles in radians to degrees: 1 rad; 0.25 rad; π rad; 2π rad; $\frac{\pi}{5}$ rad.

3 An aircraft is circling, waiting to land at an airport. Its circular path has a diameter of 20 km, and its speed is 120 m s^{-1}. How long will it take to complete one circuit of its path? In what time interval will the direction in which it is travelling change by 30°?

4 Calculate the angular speed of a masonry drill bit rotating at 720 rev min^{-1}.

5 Determine the speed of the edge of the tip of the masonry drill bit in Question 4 if the diameter of the bit is 6.0 mm.

Centripetal acceleration and force

Constant speed, changing velocity

When an object moves in a circular path, its velocity is at a tangent to the circle. If it is moving at an unchanging speed, its *speed* is constant but its *velocity* is changing, because its direction of movement is changing.

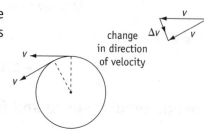

change in direction of velocity

The small arrow labelled Δv shows how the velocity vector changes from one position to the next. This arrow indicates the direction of the change in velocity, and hence the direction of the acceleration. It is directed towards the centre of the circle, and its magnitude is constant.

This acceleration is called the **centripetal acceleration**. An object can have an acceleration only if there is a force acting on it. The force that keeps an object in a circular path is called the **centripetal force**. Without such a force, the object would fly off in a straight line, at a tangent to the circle.

A centripetal force may arise in a variety of ways. Here are some examples.

A plane banks to follow a curved path. lift lift to centre of circle	The horizontal component of the lift force pushes the plane towards the centre of the circle.
A satellite orbits the Earth. satellite mg	The Earth's gravitational pull on the satellite is directed towards the centre of the Earth.
An electron orbits the nucleus of an atom. electron⁻ +	The electrostatic attraction of the nucleus pulls the electron towards it.

✓ *Quick check 1*

The size of the force

In each case, the moving object is acted on by the force towards the centre of the circle, but it never gets any closer. The force must be just large enough; any smaller, and the radius will increase; any larger, and the radius will decrease.

The centripetal force needed to make an object follow a curved path depends on three factors:

- the object's mass m: the greater the mass, the greater the force needed;
- the object's speed v: the greater the speed, the greater the force needed;
- the radius r of the path: the smaller the radius, the tighter the curve and the greater the force needed.

These quantities are combined in the following equation for F:

$$\text{centripetal force } F = \frac{mv^2}{r}$$

Worked example

A light aircraft of mass 500 kg is moving at a steady speed of 120 m s^{-1} along a curved path of radius 2.0 km. What centripetal force is needed to keep it on this path?

Substitute values in the equation for F, and solve:

$$F = \frac{mv^2}{r} = \frac{500 \text{ kg} \times (120 \text{ m s}^{-1})^2}{2000 \text{ m}} = 3600 \text{ N}$$

✓ *Quick check 2, 3*

Calculating centripetal acceleration

Since acceleration $a = \dfrac{F}{m}$, we have

$$a = \frac{v^2}{r}$$

❶ Strictly speaking, it is more correct to start from $a = v^2/r$ and use $F = ma$ to deduce that $F = mv^2/r$.

Since $v = r\omega$, centripetal acceleration can also be calculated using angular speed:

$$a = r\omega^2$$

✓ *Quick check 4*

Hence

$$\text{centripetal force} = ma = mr\omega^2$$

❓ Quick check questions

1 When a car follows a curved route, what force can provide the necessary centripetal force?

2 In a hammer-throwing event an athlete whirls round a hammer of mass 4.0 kg at arm's length in a circle of radius 1.2 m. The athlete completes one revolution in 1.4 s. Estimate the tension in the thrower's arms.

❶ First find the speed of the hammer.

3 A centripetal force is needed to make a car go round a bend. Use the equation $F = mv^2/r$ to explain why a bigger force is needed for a given speed when the car is following a more sharply curved bend.

4 The gravitational acceleration near the Moon's surface is 1.6 m s^{-2}. Calculate the speed of a satellite orbiting the Moon close to its surface. (Radius of orbit = 1800 km.)

Gravitational fields

The Earth has a **gravitational field**. This means that, if an object with mass is placed anywhere in that field, it will feel a force – the pull of the Earth's gravity. This force has another name – the **weight** of the object. A gravitational field is a field of force.

Representing a field

Field lines (lines of force) represent a gravitational field.

- The arrows show the direction of the force on a mass placed in the field.
- Lines closer together represent a stronger field.

Near the Earth's surface, the field is uniform. The field lines are effectively parallel; the force on an object is the same at all positions in the field.

On a larger scale, the Earth has a radial field. The field lines diverge; the field gets weaker the further we move away from the surface.

For a uniform sphere, the external field is the same as if all of its mass were concentrated at its centre.

✓ Quick check 1

Defining field strength

The **gravitational field strength** g at a point in a field is the force per unit mass that acts on an object placed at that point.

$$g = \frac{F}{m} \quad \text{or} \quad F = mg$$

This is the familiar equation used to calculate the weight of an object of mass m.

On the surface of the Earth, g has the approximate value

$$g = 9.8 \text{ N kg}^{-1}$$

This varies only slightly over the surface of the Earth.

Note that this value is the same as that of the acceleration of free fall, 9.8 m s^{-2}.

The force that makes an object fall is gravity. Comparing $F = mg$ with $F = ma$ shows that $a = g$.

✓ Quick check 2

Newton's law of gravitation

Newton's law tells us how to calculate the gravitational force F between two objects of masses m_1 and m_2 separated by a distance r:

$$F = \frac{Gm_1 m_2}{r^2}$$

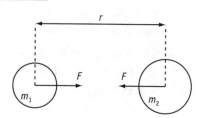

G is the **universal gravitational constant**. It has the same value everywhere in the universe. $G = 6.67 \times 10^{-11}$ N m^2 kg^{-2}.

This is an example of an *inverse square law*: F is proportional to $\frac{1}{r^2}$.

The objects are *point masses*, as if all of an object's mass is concentrated at its centre of mass. Each of the two objects feels the same force (even if their masses are different), but in opposite directions. They are an *equal and opposite pair* of forces, as described by Newton's third law of motion.

▶▶ *Centre of gravity and centre of mass – see Revise AS Physics, page 29.*

✓ **Quick check 3**

g for a point mass

For a point mass m, the gravitational field strength g at a distance r is

$$g = \frac{Gm}{r^2}$$

Worked example

Find the mass of the Earth, given that $g = 9.8$ N kg^{-1} at its surface. (Radius of the Earth $= 6.4 \times 10^6$ m, $G = 6.67 \times 10^{-11}$ N m^2 kg^{-2}.)

Step 1 Rearrange the equation $g = \frac{Gm}{r^2}$: $m = \frac{gr^2}{G}$

Step 2 Substitute values for g, r and G, and calculate the result:

$$m = \frac{9.8 \text{ N kg}^{-1} \times (6.4 \times 10^6 \text{ m})^2}{6.67 \times 10^{-11} \text{ N m}^2 \text{ kg}^{-2}} = 6.0 \times 10^{24} \text{ kg}$$

✓ **Quick check 4**

? Quick check questions

$G = 6.67 \times 10^{-11}$ N m^2 kg^{-2}

1 Explain the following. When you go upstairs, your weight is effectively unchanged; if you climb Mount Everest, your weight decreases very slightly; if you are in a spacecraft 200 km above the Earth's surface, your weight is significantly less than on the surface.

2 The Moon's gravitational field strength is 1.6 N kg^{-1}. Calculate the weight of a 5.0 kg rock on the Moon.

3 Two asteroids, of masses 4.0×10^{10} kg and 8.0×10^{10} kg, are separated by 20 km in space. Calculate the gravitational force each exerts on the other. Draw a diagram to show the directions of these forces.

4 The mass of Mars is 6.4×10^{23} kg and its radius is 3.4×10^6 m. Calculate the gravitational field strength on the surface of Mars.

Gravitational potential

Work needs to be done against the force of gravity to move a mass away from the Earth. This results in an increase in its gravitational potential energy E_P.

For small movements of a mass m in the Earth's gravitational field, we know that

$$\Delta E_P = mg\Delta h$$

For large movements we cannot use this formula, because g is not constant – field strength decreases with increasing distance from a planet or object. The idea of **gravitational potential** helps us deal with large movements in gravitational fields.

Defining gravitational potential

The gravitational potential, V, at a point in a gravitational field is the potential energy per unit mass (i.e. per kg) at that point. It has units J kg^{-1}.

$$V = \frac{E_P}{m} \quad \text{or} \quad E_P = mV$$

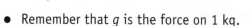

✓ *Quick check 1*

The gravitational potential at a point can also be defined as the work done per unit mass (i.e. per kg) in taking a small mass to infinity from that point.

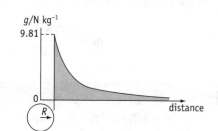

- At or above the Earth's surface, g varies with distance according to $g = \dfrac{GM}{r^2}$ (an inverse square law).

- Remember that g is the force on 1 kg.

- The area under a force–distance graph gives the work done.

- Therefore, the area shaded under the graph gives the work done to take 1 kg from the Earth's surface to infinity (provided we think of the distance axis as going on for ever!).

- This is the potential at the Earth's surface.

The area can be worked out precisely using a mathematical process of integration. You are not expected to be able to do this, but the result is important: at any distance r from the centre of a large mass M, the potential V is given by

$$V = \frac{-GM}{r}$$

The minus sign is important. We might be happy with using the Earth's surface as a zero level, but Martians, Venusians, the Borg, etc., don't regard the Earth as all that significant. By intergalactic agreement we instead adopt the convention that potential energy, and hence potential, is zero at infinity. For practical purposes infinity just means so far from anything that all fields are weak enough to ignore.

We must give an object energy in order to lift it up towards infinity. An object in a gravitational field will therefore have negative potential energy, hence the minus.

If an object is taken from one place in a gravitational field to another, the work done is equal to the *difference* in potential between the two places.

✓ *Quick check 2, 3*

Worked example

Calculate the gravitational potential at the surface of the Earth, and hence find the work done to take a 1000 kg spacecraft from the Earth's surface to outer space where the Earth's gravitational field is negligible. Neglect the effect of the other planets and the Sun. $G = 6.7 \times 10^{-11}$ N m^2 kg^{-2}; mass of Earth = 6.0×10^{24} kg; radius of Earth = 6400 km.

Step 1 Substitute the values given in $V = \dfrac{-GM}{r}$:

$$V = \frac{-6.7 \times 10^{-11}\, \text{N m}^2\ \text{kg}^{-2} \times 6.0 \times 10^{24}\ \text{kg}}{6.4 \times 10^6\, \text{m}}$$

$$= -63 \times 10^6\ \text{J}$$

Step 2 Work done per kg = difference in potential
= potential at infinity – potential at Earth's surface
= 0 – (–63 × 10^6) J
= 63 × 10^6 J

Step 3 Work done on 1000 kg = 1000 × 63 × 10^6 J = **63 × 10^9 J**

Potential and field strength

If a 1 kg mass is moved a small distance Δr, its potential will change by ΔV. The change in potential equals the work done on 1 kg, which is the force on 1 kg times the distance moved:

$$-\Delta V = g \times \Delta r$$

So the gravitational field strength g at any distance r can be found using

$$g = \frac{-\Delta V}{\Delta r} = \textbf{slope of the graph of } V \textbf{ against } r$$

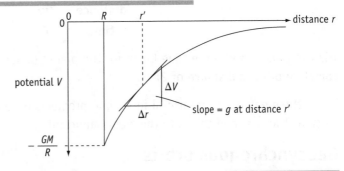

✓ *Quick check 4*

? ## Quick check questions

Take $G = 6.67 \times 10^{-11}$ N m^2 kg^{-2}; mass of Earth = 6.00×10^{24} kg; radius of Earth = 6400 km.

1   The potential energy of a 5.0 kg mass at a point in the Earth's gravitational field is 4300 J. Calculate the potential at the point.

2   Calculate the gravitational potential at the surface of the Moon. (Take mass of Moon = 7.4×10^{22} kg; radius of moon = 1.7×10^6 m.)

3   The gravitational potential at the Earth's surface is –62.5 MJ kg^{-1}. Determine the work done in taking a mass of 2400 kg from the surface of the Earth to a point in the Earth's gravitational field where the potential is –52.6 MJ kg^{-1}.

4   Use the graph of the variation of gravitational potential with distance from the Earth to estimate the gravitational field strength at a distance of 20×10^6 m from the centre of the Earth. (Start by drawing a tangent to the curve.)

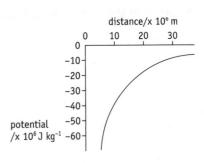

Planets and satellites

The motion of planets around the Sun and of satellites around planets can be analysed by combining our knowledge of circular motion with a knowledge of gravitational fields. We assume that planets move in circular orbits, although in reality their orbits are slightly elliptical. Planets are themselves satellites of the Sun.

Equations for planetary and satellite motion

A centripetal force acts on a satellite to keep it moving in a circle. The only force acting on the satellite is the force of gravity, so this must provide the centripetal force.

$$\frac{mv^2}{r} = \frac{GMm}{r^2}$$

r and m cancel, leaving

$$v^2 = \frac{GM}{r}$$

Also,

$$v = \frac{\text{distance}}{\text{time}} = \frac{2\pi r}{T}$$

T is the time period – the time taken for the planet or satellite to make one complete orbit, a distance of $2\pi r$.

These three equations are useful in solving problems on planetary or satellite motion. The first and third are the most important.

Geosynchronous orbits

Geosynchronous orbits are also called **geostationary orbits** or 'parking' orbits. A satellite in a geosynchronous orbit will always remain above the same place on the equator. This means that it can be used for relaying TV, telephone and other telecommunications signals from one place on the Earth's surface to another, for example from Europe to North America. The satellite must

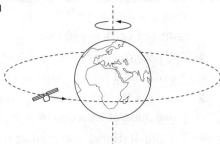

- have a time period of 24 hours;
- be in orbit above the equator;
- move in the same direction as the Earth is turning.

Worked example

Calculate the height above the Earth's surface (altitude) for a satellite to be in geosynchronous orbit. Mass of Earth = 6.0×10^{24} kg, $G = 6.7 \times 10^{-11}$ N m^2 kg^{-2}.

Step 1 Combine the formulae $v^2 = \dfrac{GM}{r}$ and $v = \dfrac{2\pi r}{T}$:

$$\frac{4\pi^2 r^2}{T^2} = \frac{GM}{r}$$

Step 2 Rearrange this equation:

$$r^3 = \frac{GMT^2}{4\pi^2}$$

Step 3 Substitute values for G, M and T, first converting T from 24 hours to seconds:

$$24\text{ h} = 24 \times 60 \times 60\text{ s} = 86400\text{ s}$$

$$r^3 = \frac{6.7 \times 10^{-11} \times 6.0 \times 10^{24} \times 86400^2}{4\pi^2}$$

> ◖ Remember to use the EXP button for 'times 10 to the power of'.

Step 4 Work out the result on your calculator. Take care: there are a lot of functions here! Pressing the right buttons gives $r = 42.4 \times 10^6$ m.

Step 5 Take away the radius of the Earth:

$$\text{altitude} = (42.4 \times 10^6 \text{ m} - 6.4 \times 10^6 \text{ m}) = 36 \times 10^6 \text{ m or } 36000 \text{ km}$$

> ◖ Get as far as possible using algebra before substituting any of the numbers.

> ✓ *Quick check 1–3*

Polar orbiting satellites

Some satellites orbit the poles. Their time period depends on their height. They 'scan' the whole surface of the Earth as it rotates under the orbiting satellite. Polar orbiting satellites are used for:

- meteorology and weather forecasting,
- military surveillance,
- navigation,
- location of the Earth's resources.

❓ Quick check questions

Take $G = 6.67 \times 10^{-11}$ N m^2 kg^{-2}; mass of Earth = 6.00×10^{24} kg; radius of Earth = 6400 km.

1 The period of the Moon around the Earth is 27.3 days.

   a Calculate the number of seconds in 27.3 days.

   b Calculate the radius of the Moon's orbit around the Earth.

2 A satellite is put in orbit 600 km above the Earth. Calculate its speed in m s^{-1} and its period.

3 The mass of Mars is 6.42×10^{23} kg and its radius is 3.38×10^6 m. A satellite with a period of 120 minutes is to be placed in orbit around Mars. Calculate its height above the surface of Mars.

> ◖ Start with Step 1 in the worked example.

Electric fields

Gravitational fields are created by objects with mass. **Electric fields** are created by objects with electric charge. There is only one type of mass, but there are two types of charge, *positive* and *negative*. Therefore electrostatic forces can be *attractive* or *repulsive*, whereas gravitational forces are always attractive.

Field lines

An electric field can be represented by **field lines**, rather like a gravitational field.

- Arrows show the direction of the force on a *positive* charge placed in the field.
- Arrows come out of positive charges, and go into negative charges.
- Lines closer together represent a stronger field.

isolated positive charge

isolated negative charge

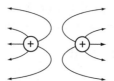

Like charges repel

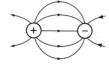

Unlike charges attract

Outside an isolated charged, conducting sphere, the field is the same as that of a point charge at its centre.

Between two charged, parallel plates, the field is uniform.

With more charge, the field is stronger.

With plates further apart, the field is weaker.

Electric field strength

✓ Quick check 1

An electric field is a field of force. Any charged object placed in the field will feel a force. To define the **electric field strength** at a point in the field, picture placing a small positive charge Q there. Measure the force F acting on the charge. Then

> **electric field strength = force per unit charge** $\qquad E = \dfrac{F}{Q}$

The unit of electric charge is the *coulomb* (C). The unit of E is therefore *newtons per coulomb* (N C^{-1}).

✓ Quick check 2

Charged parallel plates

There is a uniform electric field between a pair of parallel plates. The plates can be charged by applying a voltage across them. The greater the voltage, the stronger the field.

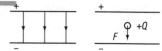

$$\text{strength of field } E = \frac{V}{d}$$

Therefore electric field strength can be measured in volts per metre ($V\ m^{-1}$) *or* in newtons per coulomb ($N\ C^{-1}$).

Now we have two equations for *E*:

$$E = \frac{F}{Q} \quad \text{and} \quad E = \frac{V}{d}$$

Putting these equal gives $\dfrac{F}{Q} = \dfrac{V}{d}$, and hence

$$Fd = QV$$

Thus the work done (*Fd*) in moving a charge *Q* through p.d. *V* is equal to *QV*. This is the equation that defines the volt: $W = QV$ (see Revise AS Physics, page 63).

Motion of a charged particle in a uniform electric field

In a vacuum, an electron enters a uniform electric field between two parallel metal plates with a horizontal speed (parallel to the plates) of *v*. The p.d. across the field is *V*. The electron experiences a constant downward force, *F*, of magnitude *QE* towards the positively charged plate, where $E = V/d$. Since the force is constant, the acceleration, *a*, towards the plate is constant. The horizontal component, *v*, of the electron's speed does not change. There are no air molecules to slow the electron down.

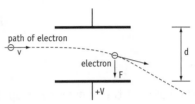

Since there is a constant vertical acceleration and a constant horizontal speed, the path of the electron is a parabola and not part of a circle. (Compare this with the path of a charged particle in a magnetic field, which is circular.)

▶▶ *This situation is like that of a projectile fired horizontally in a gravitational field without air resistance: see Revise AS Physics, page 36.*

To calculate the downward acceleration:

$F = ma = QE = QV/d$, therefore $a = QV/md$

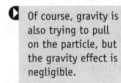

Of course, gravity is also trying to pull on the particle, but the gravity effect is negligible.

You can apply the same ideas to any charge *Q* in an electric field. If the particle were a proton, it would move along and upwards, though with less acceleration because of its greater mass.

? ## Quick check questions

1 Copy the diagram, which shows two charged, parallel metal plates. Add field lines to show the electric field between the plates. Explain how your diagram shows that this field is uniform.

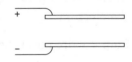

2 An electron is moving through an electric field of strength $10\ kN\ C^{-1}$. What is the electric force on it? (Charge on an electron $e = 1.6 \times 10^{-19}$ C.)

3 Two parallel plates, 20 cm apart, are connected to the terminals of a 60 V power supply. Calculate the electric field strength in the space between them.

4 The electric field strength in the space between two parallel metal plates is $5000\ V\ m^{-1}$. The p.d. across the plates is doubled and the separation of the plates is halved. Determine the new electric field strength in the space between the plates.

5 A dust particle carrying a charge of 4 mC is in the space between two parallel plates separated by 5 cm. If the plates are charged to 24 V, calculate the electric force on the dust particle.

Coulomb's law

The electric field around a point charge is radial, like the gravitational field around a spherical mass. Coulomb's law tells us how to calculate the force between two point charges.

Force between two charges

The electrostatic force F between two point charges Q_1 and Q_2, separated by a distance r, is given by **Coulomb's law:**

$$F = \frac{kQ_1Q_2}{r^2}$$

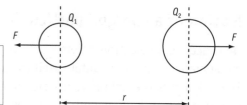

The value of the constant k is approximately 9×10^9 N m^2 C^{-2}. It is usually written as $k = \dfrac{1}{(4\pi\varepsilon_0)}$, where ε_0 is another constant called the **permittivity of free space,**

whose value is 8.85×10^{-12} F m^{-1}. This looks complicated, but is just a consequence of the system of units.

The charges are said to be *point charges*. Even if they are actually spherical, they can be considered as if all of the charge were concentrated at the centre. Each of the two charges feels the same force (even if their charges are different), but in opposite directions. They are an *equal and opposite pair* of forces, as described by Newton's third law of motion.

> ► Like Newton's law of gravitation (page 32), this is an example of an *inverse square law*: F is proportional to $1/r^2$.

> ✓ *Quick check 1*

Worked example

In an oxygen atom, the outermost electron orbits the nucleus at a distance of approximately 0.09 nm. The electron charge is $-e$ and the nuclear charge is $+8e$, where $e = 1.6 \times 10^{-19}$ C. Calculate the electrostatic force exerted by the nucleus on the electron.

Step 1 Write down the known values of quantities:
$$k = 9 \times 10^9 \text{ N m}^2 \text{ C}^{-2}$$
$$Q_1 = e = 1.6 \times 10^{-19} \text{ C}$$
$$Q_2 = 8e = 8 \times 1.6 \times 10^{-19} \text{ C} = 1.28 \times 10^{-18} \text{ C}$$
$$r = 0.09 \text{ nm} = 0.09 \times 10^{-9} \text{ m}$$

> ► There is no need to move the decimal point for r; your calculator will cope.

Step 2 Write down the equation for Coulomb's law. Substitute values and calculate F:

$$F = \frac{kQ_1Q_2}{r^2}$$
$$= \frac{(9\times10^9 \text{ N m}^2 \text{ C}^{-2})\times(1.6\times10^{-19} \text{ C})\times(1.28\times10^{-18} \text{ C})}{(0.09\times10^{-9} \text{ m})^2}$$
$$= 2.3 \times 10^{-7} \text{ N}$$

> ► Note how the units cancel correctly to leave N.

> ✓ *Quick check 2*

Field strength E for a point charge

The electric field strength E at a distance r from a point charge Q is given by

$$E = \frac{kQ}{r^2} = \frac{\left(\frac{1}{4\pi\varepsilon_0}\right)Q}{r^2} = \frac{Q}{4\pi\varepsilon_0 r^2}$$

This comes from dividing the Coulomb's law equation by Q_2. Since there is only one charge, we don't need to call it Q_1.

✓ *Quick check 3*

Electric potential and potential energy

Work has to be done to pull charges apart (if of opposite sign) or push them together (if of the same sign). The **electric potential** at a point a distance r from a charge Q is defined as the work done per coulomb in bringing a small positive charge from infinity to that point, and is given by

$$V = \frac{kQ}{r} = \frac{Q}{4\pi\varepsilon_0 r}$$

The unit of electric potential is the **volt** (V).

As for gravitational potential (page 34), the 'zero' is taken as infinity.

If a small positive charge is brought from infinity towards a positive charge, work has to be done against a repulsive force. The potential is positive.

The potential is negative for a negative charge: $V = \frac{-Q}{4\pi\varepsilon_0 r}$.

▶▶ *Gravitational and electric fields are compared on page 54.*

> ❓ *Quick check questions*
>
> 1 Draw a diagram to show two negative point charges. Add arrows to represent the force each charge exerts on the other. What can you say about the magnitudes and directions of these forces?
>
> 2 Calculate the electric force between two protons in the nucleus of an atom, separated by 1.0×10^{-15} m. (Proton charge $= +e = +1.6 \times 10^{-19}$ C.)
>
> 3 A metal sphere of radius 50 mm carries a charge of 40 mC. Calculate the electric field strength at a distance of 10 mm from the surface of the sphere. $(k = \frac{1}{4\pi\varepsilon_0} = 9 \times 10^9$ N m^2 C^{-2}.)

Electromagnetic forces

An electric current has a *magnetic field* around it. If a current flows *across* another magnetic field, the two fields interact to produce a force. If a wire carrying a current is placed at right angles to a magnetic field, there will be a force on the wire. **Fleming's left-hand rule** gives the direction of the force.

Fleming's left-hand rule

This gives the relative directions of current, field and force (i.e. *motion*). All three are at right angles to each other. Remember to use your *left* hand.

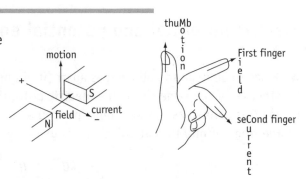

Calculating the force

Experiments with a wire and a balance show that the force *F*, in newtons (N), is proportional to three things:

- *B*, the **magnetic flux density** in **teslas** (T) – this is a measure of the strength of the magnetic field,
- *I*, the current in amps (A),
- *l*, the length of wire in the field in metres (m).

The formula is simply

$$F = BIl$$

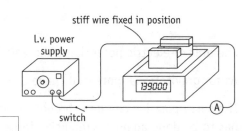

This equation applies only when the current is at 90° to the direction of the magnetic field. At other angles the force is less.

Defining the tesla

The formula *F = BIl* defines the unit of magnetic flux density, *B*. Rearranging:

$$B = \frac{F}{Il}$$

The magnetic flux density is 1 tesla (1 T) when a force of 1 newton acts on 1 metre of a straight conductor (at right angles to the magnetic flux) carrying a current of 1 ampere. The tesla is a derived unit: $1\ \text{T} = 1\ \text{N A}^{-1}\ \text{m}^{-1}$.

✓ *Quick check 1*

Force on a moving charge

When a positive charge *Q* moves with velocity *v* across a field of flux density *B*, the force *F* on the charge is

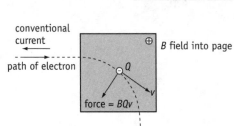

$$F = BQv$$

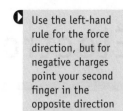
Use the left-hand rule for the force direction, but for negative charges point your second finger in the opposite direction to *v*.

A stronger field, a greater charge and a faster charge all give a bigger force.

Circular motion

When a charged particle moves at 90° to a magnetic field, the force on it is always at 90° to its velocity. (This is shown by Fleming's left-hand rule.) This is the condition needed for circular motion, so the charged particle will follow a circular path and we can describe the force as a *centripetal* force (see pages 30–31).

✓ **Quick check 2**

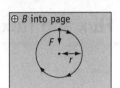

Magnetic force = mass × centripetal acceleration:

$$BQv = \frac{mv^2}{r}$$

Cancelling *v* from both sides and rearranging to find *r* gives

$$BQ = \frac{mv}{r} \quad \text{and} \quad r = \frac{mv}{BQ}$$

Looking at this equation shows that increasing the flux density will decrease the radius of the particle's orbit, i.e. the particle will go round in tighter circles.

✓ **Quick check 3–5**

In a particle accelerator called a cyclotron, sub-atomic particles from a source S are accelerated every time they cross a gap between two metal 'dees', D_1 and D_2. They move in semicircular paths of successively increasing radius, eventually leaving the cyclotron at very high speed.

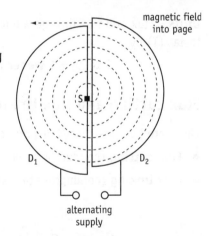

Quick check questions

1   A current of 5.0 A flows through a 2.0 m length of wire. The wire lies across a magnetic field of flux density 80 mT, as shown. What is the force on the wire? In which direction does the force act?

2   What force acts on an electron moving at 1.0×10^7 m s^{-1} at 90° to a magnetic field of flux density 0.1 T? (Electron charge $e = -1.6 \times 10^{-19}$ C.)

3   An electron enters a magnetic field as shown. In which direction will the magnetic force on the electron act?

4   Calculate the radius of the orbit of the electron in Question 2. (Electron mass = 9.1×10^{-31} kg.)

5   Two electrons, moving at different speeds but in the same direction, enter a magnetic field. Which will experience the greater force? Which will move in a bigger orbit?

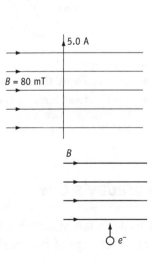

Electromagnetic induction

When a conductor is moved through a magnetic field, an e.m.f. may be generated across its ends. If it is part of a complete circuit, an induced current may flow. This is **electromagnetic induction**.

Flux and flux linkage

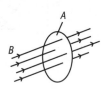

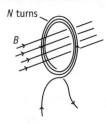

With flux density B, the flux ϕ passing through area A is given by

$$\text{flux } \phi = BA$$

For a coil of N turns, the *flux linkage* is N times the flux passing through it:

$$\text{flux linkage} = N\phi = NBA$$

> Here the flux is at 90° to the plane of A.

Units   Flux and flux linkage are measured in **webers** (Wb). These are related to teslas (T) by

$$\textbf{1 tesla = 1 weber per square metre} \quad \textbf{1 T = 1 Wb m}^{-2}$$

✓ *Quick check 1, 2*

Flux cutting and flux linking

There are two basic ways of producing an induced e.m.f.:

- **Flux cutting** (conductor moves, flux density B remains constant)
- **Flux linking** (conductor stays still, B changes)

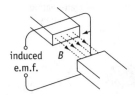

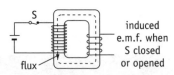

Flux cutting
- Conductor 'cuts' through constant flux.
- e.m.f. induced across ends of conductor; the faster the flux is cut, or the stronger the field, the greater the e.m.f.

Flux linking
- Magnetic field increases (S closed) or decreases (S opened) – flux linking coil changes.
- e.m.f. induced across ends of coil.
- The faster the flux changes, or the greater the flux or number of turns, the greater the e.m.f.

Faraday's law

Faraday's law states that the magnitude of the induced e.m.f (symbol ϵ) equals the rate of change of flux linking or flux cutting. For flux linking,

$$\epsilon = \frac{\textbf{change in flux linkage}}{\textbf{time taken}} = \frac{N\Delta\phi}{\Delta t}$$

> ϵ here is e.m.f. Do not confuse it with energy or electric field strength.

This gives the magnitude of the e.m.f. induced when the flux through a coil of N turns changes by $\Delta\phi$ webers in a time Δt seconds.

✓ *Quick check 3, 4*

When a conductor with a length l cuts through a field of flux density B at 90° at a speed v, the magnitude of the induced e.m.f. is given by

$$\epsilon = Blv$$

✓ *Quick check 5*

Worked example

In the ignition coil of a car, a magnetic flux linking with 12000 turns changes by 6.2 mWb (6.2×10^{-3} Wb) in 5.0 ms (5×10^{-3} s). Calculate the voltage induced.

Step 1 This is flux linking, so use $\epsilon = \dfrac{N\Delta\phi}{\Delta t}$.

Step 2 Substitute values: $\epsilon = \dfrac{12000 \times 6.2 \times 10^{-3}}{5.0 \times 10^{-3}}$.

Step 3 Use your calculator to find ϵ: $\epsilon = 15000$ V.

▶ *For the difference between p.d. and e.m.f., see Revise AS Physics, page 71.*

> Note that a suddenly collapsing field can give rise to a huge voltage.

✓ *Quick check 4*

Lenz's law

This law determines the direction in which an induced current flows, or the polarity of an induced e.m.f. An induced current flows in a direction to oppose the change producing it. This is **Lenz's law**.

For example, if a straight conductor is moved across a magnetic field, an induced current flows in it. There is a force on this current, and this force opposes the original force moving the conductor across the field.

You can use **Fleming's right-hand rule** to determine the direction of an induced current. Thumb and fingers represent the same quantities as in the left-hand rule, but in this case using the right hand.

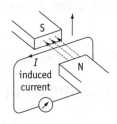

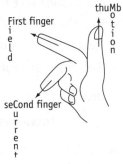

? Quick check questions

1 2.0×10^{-3} Wb of magnetic flux pass through a square area 10 cm × 10 cm, at 90° to the flux. What is the flux density of this magnetic field?

2 What is the flux linkage of a circular coil of radius 5.0 cm, consisting of 50 turns of wire, placed perpendicular to a magnetic field of flux density 200 mT?

3 Determine the e.m.f. induced across the ends of the coil in Question 2 when it is removed completely from the field in 0.15 s.

4 A coil of wire is being rotated in a magnetic field. Which of the following will increase the e.m.f. induced across the coil: increasing the flux density of the field; increasing the rate of rotation; reversing the direction of rotation; reducing the resistance of the coil by using thicker wire?

5 The metal wings of an aircraft cut through the Earth's magnetic field at 90°. The speed of the aircraft is 140 m s^{-1} and the Earth's magnetic flux density is 4.7×10^{-5} T. Calculate the voltage induced between the wing tips if they are 25 m apart.

Mass–energy conservation

Einstein recognised that mass and energy are related by the equation $E = mc^2$, where c is the speed of light in free space. In most of the physics you study and in everyday situations this is not particularly useful, which is why it seems such a weird idea, but at an atomic or nuclear level the equivalence of mass and energy is vitally important.

Mass and energy units

The masses of subatomic particles are very small; it is convenient to express them in **atomic mass units (u)**, rather than kg:

$$1\ u = 1.66 \times 10^{-27}\ kg$$

Using $E = mc^2$ where $c = 3.0 \times 10^8$ m s^{-1}, we can find the energy equivalent of 1 u:

$$1\ u = 1.66 \times 10^{-27}\ kg \times (3.0 \times 10^8\ m\ s^{-1})^2 = 1.49 \times 10^{-10}\ J$$

Remembering that small amounts of energy may be expressed in *electronvolts* rather than joules, where 1 eV = 1.6×10^{-19} J, we find that

$$1\ u = 931\ MeV$$

▶▶ *For electronvolts, refer back to Revise AS Physics, page 16.*

✓ *Quick check 1*

Disappearing mass

It is a strange fact that, for any nucleus, the mass of the nucleus is less than the sum of the masses of its parts! For example, for a carbon nucleus:

- Rest mass of proton = 1.673×10^{-27} kg = 1.007 28 u
- Rest mass of neutron = 1.675×10^{-27} kg = 1.008 67 u

A carbon nucleus has 6 protons and 6 neutrons, therefore:

$$\textbf{total mass} = (6 \times 1.007\ 28) + (6 \times 1.008\ 67) = 12.0957\ u$$

But a carbon nucleus has a mass of 11.9967 u. We appear to have 'lost' 0.0990 u. This 'lost' mass is called the **mass difference** or **mass defect**.

A nucleus has less energy than its components had before they joined together. The nucleons of a nucleus are bound together. Energy is needed to separate them. The **binding energy** of a nucleus is the energy needed to separate a nucleus into its individual nucleons. For a carbon nucleus:

- Binding energy = $0.0990 \times 931.3 = 92.2$ MeV
- Binding energy *per nucleon* = 92.2/12 = 7.68 MeV

The decrease in mass Δm when nucleons join together is accounted for by the appearance of an amount of energy ΔE. These are related by Einstein's equation:

$$\Delta E = \Delta m \times c^2$$

The **rest mass** of a particle (see above) is its mass when at rest. A *moving* particle has kinetic energy, and its mass is greater than its rest mass.

> ◖ It may help to think of this as the *unbinding energy* of the nucleus.

✓ *Quick check 2, 3*

Nuclear transformations

When atomic nuclei are bombarded with fast-moving atomic particles, they sometimes change or *transform* into different nuclei. When an alpha particle ($^4_2$He) is absorbed by a nitrogen nucleus ($^{14}_7$N), a nucleus of an oxygen isotope is formed. We can represent this change by an equation:

$$^{14}_7\text{N} + ^4_2\text{He} \rightarrow ^{17}_8\text{O} + ^1_1\text{H}$$

The total rest mass of the nuclei on each side of this equation is found to be:

- 13.999 23 + 4.001 51 = 18.000 74 u, on the left-hand side ('before')
- 16.994 74 + 1.007 28 = 18.002 02 u, on the right-hand side ('after')

The total mass after the transformation is greater than the original total mass. The difference is the kinetic energy supplied by the alpha particle:

18.002 02 u – 18.000 74 u = 0.001 28 u = 1.19 MeV

In radioactive decay, where a nucleus emits one or more particles,

mass of particles before decay > mass of particles after decay

Worked example

A neutron decays to become a proton and an electron. How much energy is released? (Values of rest mass are shown in the table. Inspection shows that the proton and electron together have less mass than the neutron.)

> ● Note that in this example we will work in kg.

particle	rest mass / kg
neutron, n	$m_n = 1.674\ 928 \times 10^{-27}$
proton, p	$m_p = 1.672\ 623 \times 10^{-27}$
electron, e	$m_e = 0.000\ 911 \times 10^{-27}$

Step 1 Write down an equation for the reaction:

$$n \rightarrow p + e$$

> ● This equation is sometimes written $^1_0 n \rightarrow ^1_1 H + ^0_{-1} e$.

Step 2 Calculate the loss in mass, Δm:

$$\Delta m = m_n - (m_p + m_e) = 1.394 \times 10^{-30}\text{ kg}$$

Step 3 Calculate the energy ΔE released:

$$\Delta E = \Delta m \times c^2 = 1.394 \times 10^{-30}\text{ kg} \times (3.00 \times 10^8\text{ m s}^{-1})^2 = 1.25 \times 10^{-13}\text{ J}$$

> ✓ *Quick check 4*

? Quick check questions

1 The rest mass of a neutron is $1.674\ 928 \times 10^{-27}$ kg. What is this in atomic mass units?

2 A fast-moving electron may be captured by a proton to form a neutron. However, a stationary electron cannot be captured. Explain why not, using ideas about mass–energy conservation.

> ● You may wish to refer to the table of mass values above.

3 The Sun radiates energy into space at the rate of 4.0×10^{26} W. By how much does its mass decrease each second? ($c = 3.0 \times 10^8$ m s^{-1}.)

4 In nuclear fission (see next page), a 'mother' nucleus splits to form two 'daughter' nuclei; some neutrons are also released. What can you say about the mass of these products, compared to that of the mother nucleus?

Fusion and fission

For the carbon nucleus on page 46, the binding energy per nucleon was found to be about 7.7 MeV. The graph shows the binding energy per nucleon of all nuclei. Iron (Fe) is at the highest point; its nucleons are most tightly bound together.

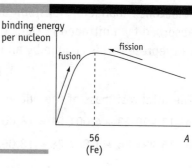

Nuclear fusion

In **nuclear fusion**, small nuclei bind together to form a bigger nucleus. Energy is released; the nucleons are more tightly bound together.

For example, if deuterium ($^2_1$H) and tritium ($^3_1$H) react together,

$$^2_1\text{H} + ^3_1\text{H} \rightarrow ^4_2\text{He} + ^1_0\text{n} + E$$

The energy E required to 'balance' the equation is about 17.5 MeV.

Fusion will occur only if the nuclei can be made to collide at very high speed. This would require extremely high temperatures, of the order of 10^8 K.

✓ *Quick check 1*

Nuclear fission

In **nuclear fission**, a large nucleus (such as uranium-235) 'captures' a neutron and splits to form two or more smaller nuclei. Again, energy is released; the nucleons are more tightly bound together in the resulting nuclei.

Many nuclear fission reactions are possible, for example:

$$^{235}_{92}\text{U} + ^1_0\text{n} \rightarrow ^{95}_{42}\text{Mo} + ^{139}_{57}\text{La} + 2\ ^1_0\text{n} + E$$

E is about 200 MeV per fission.

✓ *Quick check 2*

Chain reaction and critical mass

Note that in the above fission reaction two neutrons are released. These can go on to collide with other uranium nuclei to cause more fission – and a **chain reaction** is possible unless the number of neutrons is kept under control.

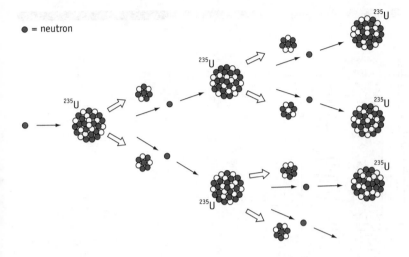

● = neutron

In fact, neutrons are lost by escaping from the surface of the uranium, and a chain reaction will not start if the lump of uranium is too small. As the mass increases the surface area/volume ratio *decreases*. To put it another way, there are more neutrons available inside to produce fission compared to the number escaping, so a chain reaction will occur if the lump of uranium is above a **critical mass**.

❓ Quick check questions

1 Show that the energy E released in the reaction

$$_1^2\text{H} + _1^3\text{H} \rightarrow _2^4\text{He} + _0^1\text{n} + E$$

is 17.5 MeV.

(Use the following masses (all $\times 10^{-27}$ kg): deuterium ($_1^2\text{H}$) 3.345, tritium ($_1^3\text{H}$) 5.008, helium ($_2^4\text{He}$) 6.647, neutron ($_0^1\text{n}$) 1.675.)

2 Comparing the figures given opposite for the energy released per fusion reaction (17.5 MeV) and per fission reaction (200 MeV), which gives more energy per kg of fuel? Show your working.

Thermal nuclear reactors and transmutation

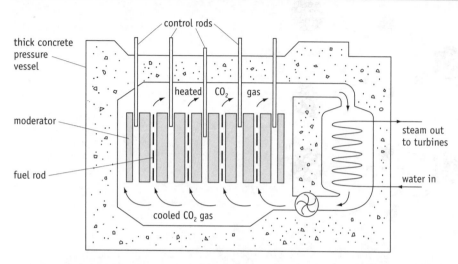

In a nuclear reactor the fuel is a fissionable material such as uranium-235 (^{235}U). Natural uranium consists of 99.3% ^{238}U and 0.7% ^{235}U. ^{235}U is the more important isotope because it undergoes fission much more easily than ^{238}U.

The fuel in a reactor consists of rods of natural uranium or pellets of uranium dioxide. The uranium in pellets is **enriched** so it has more than 0.7% of ^{235}U.

^{235}U will undergo fission only by the action of relatively *slow* neutrons that have kinetic energies similar to those of the surrounding atoms, so the fast neutrons from the fission reaction must be slowed down by a **moderator**. ^{238}U is unlikely to undergo fission by either fast neutrons (such as those released during ^{235}U fission) or slow neutrons.

For fission to continue at a constant rate without going out of control, only one of the neutrons produced at each fission must go on to cause another fission (the **critical** condition). **Control rods** lowered into the reactor core between the fuel rods absorb neutrons and control the rate of fission.

A **coolant** under pressure passes through the reactor to remove heat energy, which is transferred to water in a heat exchanger. The water turns to steam which drives turbine-generators to produce electricity.

	Moderator	Coolant	Control rod
What it does	slows neutrons so they can cause fission in ^{235}U	removes heat from reactor	controls rate of fission
How it does it	neutrons collide with moderator atoms and lose much of their E_K	passes through reactor core, taking thermal energy from hot fuel	absorbs neutrons
Factors influencing choice of materials	ability to slow neutrons by having 'light' nuclei; high melting point (if solid); easy availability	high specific heat capacity; non-corrosive; non-flammable	ability to absorb neutrons; strength; high melting point

	Moderator	Coolant	Control rod
Materials used (AGR: advanced gas-cooled reactor; PWR: pressurised water reactor)	carbon (as graphite, in Magnox and AGR); water (PWR); heavy water (actually deuterium oxide, in heavy water reactors)	carbon dioxide (CO_2), 400°C (Magnox); CO_2 under pressure, 660°C (AGR); water under pressure, 324°C (PWR); heavy water	boron (in the form of boron steel); cadmium also absorbs neutrons

✓ *Quick check 1, 2*

Artificial transmutation

Transmutation is the term given to the production of radioactive nuclides that do not occur in nature. They are made by bombarding stable nuclides with high-energy particles, for example neutrons, protons and deuterons. The particles can be given high energies in particle accelerators.

Most radionuclides used in medicine are produced by placing a sample of the stable target material in a nuclear reactor. The vast supply of neutrons in the reactor causes neutron reactions to take place in the atoms of the sample.

For example, in the conversion of ^{130}tellurium to ^{131}iodine,

$$^{130}_{52}\text{Te} + ^{1}_{0}\text{n} \rightarrow ^{131}_{52}\text{Te} + \gamma \rightarrow ^{131}_{53}\text{I} + \beta^{-}$$

^{130}tellurium is irradiated with neutrons and transforms into ^{131}tellurium (and gamma emission). This decays by beta emission into ^{131}iodine, which is used in medical tracer studies, particularly in determining the activity of the thyroid gland.

▶▶ *More about radioactive decay on pages 64–67.*

Artificial transmutation is used to produce hundreds of different radionuclides that can be matched to specific applications in medicine and industry:

- Tracers in medicine for measuring, e.g., volumes of blood, circulation times
- Radionuclide imaging of parts of the body
- Radiotherapy: destroying tumours using gamma rays
- Tracers for detecting the position of, and leaks from, underground pipelines
- Tracers for studying river pollution, uptake of plant nutrients, root growth
- Sterilisation of medical instruments by gamma rays
- Measurement of wear in machinery, and use of gamma rays in non-destructive testing, e.g. detection of cracks in aircraft wings.

In medical applications, half-lives must be long enough for a tracer to reach the organ to be imaged but not so long that unnecessary exposure levels are reached.

▶▶ *For more on half-life see page 67.*

? Quick check questions

1 Enriching uranium so that it contains about 1% of ^{235}U is an expensive process. What are the benefits?

2 For a thermal fission reactor, explain the function of:

   a the moderator

   b the coolant

   c the control rods.

Nuclear safety

Safety of nuclear reactors

The fission process in a nuclear reactor produces highly radioactive fission products. The ionising radiation from the fuel can produce biological damage that may lead to cancer and hereditary defects.

Reactors are designed and operated to ensure that exposure to ionising radiation is as low as can be reasonably achieved. After a few years in a reactor, the fuel has to be replaced. The irradiated or 'spent' fuel must be handled carefully, and the small percentage of highly radioactive waste must be disposed of safely.

What safety measures are in place?

The fuel

- Solid fuel is inherently safer than liquid fuel, since solids cannot leak.
- The fuel is in the form of uranium metal or pellets of uranium dioxide sealed in metal cans or tubes. Before use in the reactor the fuel is safe to handle. During use the fission products remain locked in the atomic structure of the fuel within the metal cans.

Shielding

- Primary protective **shielding** is provided by the fuel can (cladding), the moderator and the coolant.
- A leakproof concrete **biological shield** several metres thick surrounds the reactor and absorbs neutrons and gamma radiation released during fission. In many reactors the shield also acts as a **pressure vessel** for the coolant.
- An **exclusion zone** is maintained around the reactor that would allow for dilution and dispersal of any released radioactive material before it reached any built-up area.

Emergency shutdown

- In the event of the rate of fission increasing too fast, the reactor can be made safe by driving the control rods into the core (in some reactors they fall under gravity).
- An emergency core cooling system comes into operation if there is a loss of coolant.
- If anyone tried to interfere with anything that would affect reactor safety, the reactor would automatically shut down.

Handling of spent fuel

- Spent fuel taken from the reactor is radioactive and is stored in cooling ponds at the power station to allow much of the short-term radioactivity to die away.

- It is then transported to a reprocessing plant in immensely strong steel flasks.

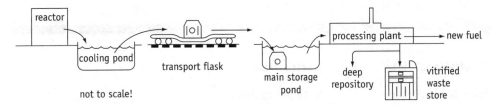

- The fuel is then stored under water for a further period before reprocessing.

- Finally, the cladding is removed and the fuel is separated into uranium and plutonium and a small percentage of highly radioactive waste. (96% of spent Magnox fuel is uranium that is processed into new fuel.)

Disposal of radioactive waste

Storage and eventual disposal must be secure and safe to the environment. Sites used for storage and disposal will require continual monitoring. Depending on how radioactive it is, radioactive waste is placed in one of three categories:

Low-level waste (95–96% by volume)	Intermediate-level waste (4–5%)	High-level waste (<0.1%)
Used wrapping material, used protective clothing, worn-out equipment; also cooling pond water	Fuel element cladding, sludge from treatment process, contaminated equipment, hospital radioisotopes	Unwanted, highly radioactive material (in liquid form) separated from spent fuel
Deep underground repository. After treatment, cooling pond water is released to environment	Encasing in cement in steel drums. Future storage deep underground in stable rock formation with low water flow	Converted into a powder, then vitrification (fused into glass blocks). Stored in air-cooled containers for 50 years for radioactivity to fall, then deep underground in stable rock formation

✔ *Quick check 1, 2*

? *Quick check questions*

1 List the advantages and disadvantages of transporting a flask of high-level radioactive waste by each of road, rail, air and sea.

2 Draw a flow chart to show the stages a fuel element goes through once its useful life in a reactor is over.

Comparing gravitational and electric fields

	Gravitational field	Electric field
Field strength equation	force per kilogram $$g = \frac{F}{m}$$	force per coulomb $$E = \frac{F}{Q}$$
Radial field	point mass or spherical mass	point charge or charged sphere
Inverse square law	Newton's law: $F = \dfrac{Gm_1 m_2}{r^2}$	Coulomb's law: $F = \dfrac{kQ_1 Q_2}{r^2}$
Constant	$G = 6.67 \times 10^{-11}$ N m^2 kg^{-2}	$k = 9 \times 10^9$ N m^2 C^{-2}
Potential	$V = -\dfrac{GM}{r}$	$V = \dfrac{\pm kQ}{r}$
Uniform field	near surface of Earth $g \sim 9.8$ N kg^{-1}	between charged parallel plates $$E = \frac{V}{d}$$
Motion of particle in uniform vertical field	constant vertical acceleration (g), constant horizontal speed, parabolic path	constant vertical acceleration, constant horizontal speed, parabolic path

The equations $g = \dfrac{F}{m}$ and $E = \dfrac{F}{Q}$ can be applied in *any* field (gravitational or electric, respectively). The other equations can be applied only in radial or uniform fields, as appropriate.

Gravitational forces between masses can only be attractive. Electric forces can be attractive or repulsive.

Gravitational potential can only be negative. Electric potential can be negative or positive, depending on the sign of the charge.

Module 4: end-of-module questions

1 A small mass hangs from the end of a vertical spring. It is displaced downwards and released, and oscillates up and down with simple harmonic motion. The variation with time *t* of the displacement *y* of the mass is shown in the figure.

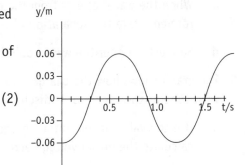

a State what is meant by *simple harmonic motion*. (2)

b For the oscillations of the mass determine the

   i amplitude

   ii period

  iii frequency

  iv maximum acceleration

   v maximum velocity. (7)

c Mark with an A on the graph one point at which the acceleration is a maximum. (1)

d Mark with a V on the graph one point at which the velocity is a maximum. (1)

2 A prototype washing machine was tested by placing it on a test bed and gradually increasing the frequency of rotation of the electric motor. The amplitude of vibration of the top surface of the washing machine was measured over the range of motor frequencies. Resonance occurred when the motor frequency was 65 Hz, with an amplitude of 1.2 mm.

a Explain what is meant by *resonance*. (2)

b Sketch a graph of amplitude (*y*-axis) against frequency (*x*-axis) for the test results. (3)

c Explain what is meant by a *damped* vibration. (1)

d On the same set of axes you used in **b**, sketch the effect of applying more damping to the vibrations. (1)

3 Laser light of wavelength 648 nm is passed through a pair of narrow parallel slits in a darkened room. A pattern of light and dark fringes is seen on a screen 5.7 m from the slits.

a Using the terms *constructive interference* and *path difference*, explain how a bright fringe is formed. (3)

b The width of ten of the fringes is found to be 28 mm. Calculate the separation of the two slits. (3)

c One of the slits is covered up. Describe how the pattern on the screen would change. (2)

4 A string is stretched horizontally. One end is moved up and down at a frequency of 30 Hz, so that a wave travels along the string. The wavelength of the wave is 4.0 cm.

  a State whether the wave is transverse or longitudinal and give a reason for your answer. (2)

  b Calculate the speed of propagation of the wave along the string. (1)

  c When the wave reflects from the ends of the string, a stationary pattern is formed. State the separation of adjacent nodes in this pattern. (1)

  d Suggest whether the wave could be polarised. (2)

5 The graph shows how the charge on a 4.0 μF capacitor changes with time as the capacitor is discharged through a resistor.

  a Use the value of the initial charge on the capacitor to calculate the initial voltage across the capacitor. (1)

  b Estimate the initial discharging current. To do this, draw a tangent to the curve at X. The slope of this tangent gives the initial discharging current. (2)

  c Using your answers to **a** and **b**, determine the resistance of the resistor. (2)

  d Another way to calculate the resistance is to use the time constant. Use the graph to find the time constant, and hence determine a value for the resistance of the resistor. (2)

  e Which of your two answers for the resistance is the more accurate? Give a reason for your answer. (2)

6 A 2000 μF capacitor is charged up until the p.d. between its plates is 10 V. It is then allowed to discharge through a 500 kΩ resistor.

  a Calculate the initial current that flows through the resistor. (1)

  b Calculate the initial charge on the capacitor. (1)

  c Calculate the time constant for the circuit. (2)

  d Sketch a graph to show how the charge on the capacitor changes with time. (2)

  e Calculate the charge on the capacitor after 500 s. (2)

7 a Jupiter has mass M; one of its moons has mass m and orbits along a circular path of radius r.

    i Write down an expression for the gravitational force F that Jupiter exerts on its moon. (1)

    ii What can you say about the gravitational force exerted by this moon on Jupiter? (1)

b The moon orbits Jupiter with speed v. Use the following data to calculate v.

mass of Jupiter $M = 1.9 \times 10^{27}$ kg
radius of moon's orbit $r = 7.0 \times 10^{5}$ km
universal gravitational constant $G = 6.67 \times 10^{-11}$ N m^2 kg^{-2} (3)

c Calculate the time taken for the moon to make one complete orbit of Jupiter. (3)

8 The gravitational potential at the surface of the Earth is -6.3×10^{7} J kg^{-1}.

a Explain the meaning of *gravitational potential* at a point in a gravitational field. (2)

b Explain why values of gravitational potential are usually given a negative sign. (1)

c Calculate the minimum energy needed to take a spacecraft of mass 2500 kg from the surface of the Earth to a height above the Earth where the gravitational potential is -4.0×10^{7} J kg^{-1}. (3)

9 In an electrostatic dust filter for a workshop, charged dust particles are blown through a uniform electric field between metal plates and are deflected onto one of the plates.

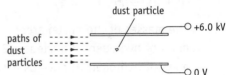

The figure shows a dust particle of mass 400×10^{-15} kg and charge $+1.0 \times 10^{-16}$ C which has entered the electric field at right angles. The potential difference across the plates is 6.0 kV and they are 12 mm apart.

a Calculate

  i the electric field strength in the region between the plates

  ii the force on the dust particle due to the electric field

  iii the acceleration of the dust particle in the direction of this force. (4)

b Copy the figure and draw an arrow on the dust particle to show the direction of the force on the dust particle due to the electric field. (1)

c Explain why the path taken by the dust particle between the plates is not part of a circle. (2)

10 The flux density of a magnetic field can be found by measuring the force on a current-carrying conductor placed in the field. In such a measurement, a 40 mm length of conductor carrying a current of 1.5 A is placed between the poles of a magnet at right angles to the field. The force acting on the conductor is found to be 0.06 N.

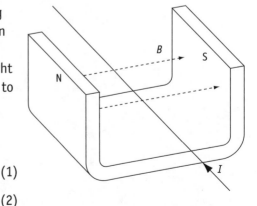

a Draw an arrow on the diagram to show the direction of the force on the conductor for the given directions of field and current. (1)

b Calculate the flux density of the field. (2)

11 The diagram shows a coil of 100 turns of wire, placed so that its plane is perpendicular to a horizontal magnetic field of flux density 0.05 T. The coil is rectangular, with sides of lengths 60 mm and 100 mm.

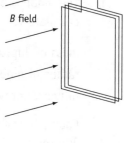

B field

a Calculate the flux passing through the coil, and its flux linkage. (3)

b The coil is slowly moved downwards through the field, so that its plane remains perpendicular to the flux. Explain why no e.m.f. is induced between its ends. (2)

c The coil is withdrawn completely from the field to a region where there is no magnetic field in a time of 80 ms. Calculate the average induced e.m.f. across the ends of the coil. (3)

12 The graph shows how the binding energy per nucleon depends on the nucleon number for different nuclei.

a Use the graph to explain why the process of nuclear fusion results in a release of energy. (3)

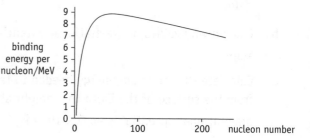

b A particular fusion reaction is

$$^2_1H + {}^1_1H \rightarrow {}^3_2He + energy$$

The masses of the nuclei are:
mass of hydrogen ^2_1H nucleus = 2.013 55 u
mass of hydrogen ^1_1H nucleus = 1.007 28 u
mass of helium ^3_2He nucleus = 3.014 93 u

Calculate the energy released in the reaction. (4)

13 a A thermal nuclear power station depends for its operation on a *chain reaction* occurring in the nuclear reactor.

  i Describe a chain reaction.

  ii Explain what is meant by *critical mass*.

  iii Explain how the chain reaction in a nuclear reactor is controlled. (7)

b Describe how the spent fuel taken from a nuclear reactor is treated and how the waste products are disposed of safely. (6)

Module 5: Nuclear instability

There are only two blocks in this module.

- **Block 5A** is about alpha, beta and gamma radiation and the experimental means of distinguishing one type of radiation from another. It looks at radioactive decay and the concept of half-life and shows how we can express radioactive decay mathematically. You may have come across some of the basic ideas in this block at GCSE.

- **Block 5B** explains what happens to nuclei when they emit alpha or beta particles or gamma radiation. It builds on the alpha particle scattering experiment that was dealt with at the very beginning of Module 1, and shows how the size of the nucleus has been estimated by bombarding nuclei with electrons and other particles.

Block 5A: Radioactivity, pages 60–67

Ideas from GCSE	Content outline of Block 5A
<ul><li>Alpha, beta and gamma radiation</li><li>Absorption by different materials</li><li>Half-life</li></ul>	<ul><li>Nature and properties of α, β, γ radiation</li><li>Background radiation</li><li>Inverse square law for γ-rays</li><li>Exponential law of decay</li><li>Half-life</li></ul>

Block 5B: Nuclear stability and probing matter, pages 68–71

Ideas from GCSE	Content outline of Block 5B
<ul><li>Nuclear equations</li></ul>	<ul><li>Nuclear equations for α, β^-, β^+, γ emission and electron capture</li><li>Probing matter by scattering</li><li>Determination of nuclear radius</li></ul>

End-of-module questions, pages 72–74

Radioactivity

Various sheets of differing materials can be placed in front of a radioactive source to find out if the radiation penetrates them easily. Also, the radiation can be passed through a magnetic field. Experiments indicate that there are three kinds of radiation: **alpha** (α) and **beta** (β) are particles, while **gamma** (γ) is high-energy, short-wavelength electromagnetic radiation.

Deflection experiments

When α, β and γ radiation are passed through a magnetic field, the α and β particles are deflected in opposite directions, showing that they have opposite charges, while γ radiation passes through undeflected. The direction and degree of deflection show that

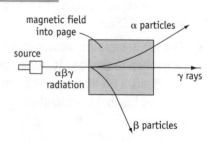

- α have positive charge,
- β have negative charge,
- β have a much smaller mass than α,
- γ have no charge.

✓ *Quick check 1*

Ionising radiation

As α, β and γ radiations pass through matter, they lose energy. Their interactions with matter cause **ionisation** – electrons are knocked from neutral atoms. The α radiation is the most strongly ionising; its range is least because of the energy absorbed.

- α radiation outside the body is relatively harmless, as it is stopped by clothes or the skin.
- An α particle emitter inside the body can be very harmful because of the ionisation damage the particles produce internally to cells.
- Outside the body, β and γ sources are more harmful than α sources because the γ rays can penetrate into the body.

Absorption experiments

The α, β and γ radiations can be identified by their relative **penetrating power** in different materials.

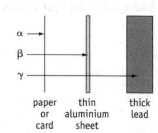

α particles:

- have a range of about 3 to 10 cm in air;
- are stopped by a thin sheet of paper.

β particles:

- have a range of about 50 cm in air;
- are stopped by a few millimetres of aluminium.

γ rays:

- have an extremely long range in air because they produce very few ions;
- are not easily absorbed but can be reduced to safe levels by several centimetres of lead or metres of concrete.

Summary of α, β and γ radiation

Type	Mass (relative)	Charge	Nature	Ionising power	Range in air	Stopped by	Deflection by magnetic field
α (alpha)	4	+2	helium nucleus	very strong	few cm	thick paper or card	small
β (beta)	0 (nearly)	−1	electron	fairly weak	about 50 cm	3 mm aluminium	large and opposite to α
γ (gamma)	0	0	electro-magnetic wave	very weak	several km	thick lead or concrete	no deflection

✓ *Quick check 1, 2*

Applications

- Smoke alarms: smoke passes between a small α source and a detector, the count rate falls and this triggers an electronic alarm.
- Monitoring thickness of sheet plastic, metal or paper: a β source (for plastic or paper) or γ source (for metal) is placed on one side of the sheet, and a detector on the other. If the thickness varies as the sheet is moved over the detector, the count rate will change.

? Quick check questions

1 Describe briefly a simple experiment to show that γ radiation is uncharged.
2 Of the three types of ionising radiation, α, β and γ, which interacts least strongly with matter as it passes through it?

Background radiation and the inverse square law

Background radiation

We all receive a certain dose of ionising radiation every year from both naturally occurring and artificial sources. Approximate exposure is given in the diagram.

Sources of **background radiation** are:

- cosmic rays from outer space (mostly high-energy protons),

- traces of radioactive material in soil and rocks, and radon gas seeping from the ground,

- radioactive material released into the environment in nuclear tests and nuclear accidents,

- radioactive waste from the nuclear power industry,

- medical and industrial uses of radioactivity.

When you do an experiment involving count rates, first measure the **background count** in the same place but without the source, using the detector you will use in the experiment. Subtract the background count from all subsequent measured count rates.

Because of the random nature of radiation emissions, be careful not to be too precise in interpreting the results of a single count experiment. For example, if a detector connected to a counter set at 100 s gave a background count of 43, the background count rate of 43/100 could reasonably be expressed as 0.4 counts per second, not as 0.43, because if the 100 s count were repeated it would probably give a count different from 43 but still close to 40.

food and drink

cosmic rays 11.5%

10%

ground and 14%
buildings

50%
radon gas
from ground

14%
medical

occupational 0.3%
fallout 0.2%
nuclear discharges < 0.1%

✓ *Quick check 1*

✓ *Quick check 2*

Inverse square law for γ rays

Gamma radiation obeys an **inverse square law**.

If I_0 is the energy per second radiated from the source, and I is the energy per second falling on unit area at a distance x,

$$I = \frac{kI_0}{x^2}$$

I is proportional to the corrected count rate, so

$$\textbf{count rate} \propto \frac{1}{\textbf{(distance from source)}^2}$$

Therefore, if you double the distance from the source, the count rate goes down by a factor of 4.

This is important in the safe handling of radioactive sources – the further you are from the source the less your dose of radiation.

- Avoid direct contact with sources.
- Handle solid sources using tongs.
- Keep at a safe distance when using sources.

✓ *Quick check 3, 4*

Investigation of inverse square law

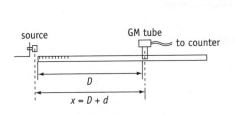
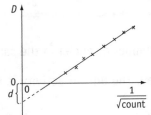

- Measure count rate over a range of distances.
- Correct for background count.
- Plot D (y axis) against $\dfrac{1}{\sqrt{\text{corrected count rate}}}$.
- If the inverse square law is obeyed, the graph is a straight line with a negative intercept d, where d is the unknown *extra* distance the γ ray travels inside the detector and inside the source. It is impossible to measure d directly.

❓ Quick check questions

1 State four sources of background radiation.

2 The background count for a radioactivity experiment was measured by taking four successive 10-second counts with a detector and counter. The results were 8, 11, 7 and 5. Estimate the background count to be subtracted from 10-second counts recorded in the experiment.

3 A detector counts only γ radiation. If the corrected count rate recorded at a distance of 200 mm from a source is 28 counts per second, what corrected count would be expected at a distance of 100 mm from the source?

4 A point source emits γ rays with equal intensity in all directions. A counter records a count rate of 3694 counts in 10 seconds when placed 20 cm from the source. What would you expect the *corrected* count rate per 10 s to be when the detector is moved to a distance of 60 cm from the source? Take the background count rate to be 40 counts in 100 seconds.

The decay constant

Radioactive decay is a *random* process. This means that it is impossible to predict when an individual nucleus will decay – now, in five minutes or in a million million years. Because sources contain large numbers of atoms, however, we can make predictions about what will happen *on average*.

Activity of a sample

The **activity**, $\frac{\Delta N}{\Delta t}$, of a sample is the average number of nuclei in the sample that decay per second, i.e. the average rate of decay. The unit of activity is the **becquerel (Bq)**.

$$1 \text{ Bq} = 1 \text{ s}^{-1} \text{ (1 decay per second)}$$

We have to consider the *average* (or *mean*) number of decays per second, because the rate fluctuates randomly. In practice, it is difficult to detect all of the decays that occur, so we may use the measured **count rate**, instead of the activity. The **corrected count rate** takes account of the background count rate.

✓ *Quick check 1*

Decay constant

Some radioactive materials decay very quickly; others decay very slowly. A measure of this difference is the **decay constant**, λ (lambda). The decay constant for a particular isotope is the probability that an individual nucleus will decay in unit time.

Units s^{-1} (or day^{-1}, or year^{-1}, etc.)

Example   An isotope has decay constant $\lambda = 0.1$ year^{-1}. We observe a single nucleus of this isotope for one year; there is a probability of 0.1 (i.e. 1 in 10) that it will decay in this time. If we observe 100 of these nuclei for a year, we would expect roughly 10 to decay.

Hence, the activity $\Delta N/\Delta t$ of a sample depends on two things:

• the decay constant λ of the isotope;

• the number of undecayed nuclei N it contains.

activity = decay constant × number of undecayed nuclei
$$\frac{\Delta N}{\Delta t} = -\lambda N$$

Worked example

A sample of radioactive carbon contains 2×10^{13} undecayed carbon nuclei. The decay constant for this isotope is 4×10^{-12} s^{-1}. What is the activity of the sample?

Substituting in the equation gives

$$-\frac{\Delta N}{\Delta t} = \lambda N = 4 \times 10^{-12} \text{ s}^{-1} \times 2 \times 10^{13} = 80 \text{ s}^{-1}$$

So the activity is 80 s^{-1}, or 80 Bq.

✓ *Quick check 2, 3*

The pattern of decay

As a sample of a radioactive substance decays, several quantities follow the same pattern:

- $\dfrac{\Delta N}{\Delta t}$, the activity of the sample;

- N, the number of undecayed nuclei;

- C, the corrected count rate.

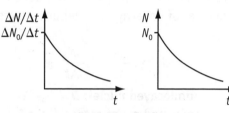

Each of these quantities starts at a certain initial value ($\Delta N_0/\Delta t$, N_0 and C_0, respectively); its value decreases rapidly at first, then more and more slowly. This is an **exponential decay**.

In practice, because radioactive decay is random and spontaneous, an experimental curve will have points scattered about the smooth theoretical curve. Also, a true exponential curve never reaches zero. However, in the case of radioactivity, the last undecayed nucleus will eventually decay, and the curve will reach zero.

✓ *Quick check 4*

❓ Quick check questions

1 A Geiger counter placed next to a sample of a radioactive material detects an average of 1.5 counts per second. Give two reasons why it would be incorrect to conclude that the sample's activity is 1.5 Bq.

2 A sample of a radioactive isotope contains 5×10^{8} undecayed nuclei. Its activity is 600 Bq. What is the decay constant for this isotope?

3 The decay constant for a radioactive isotope is 0.15 day^{-1}.

  a Convert this decay constant to s^{-1}.

  b How many undecayed nuclei of the isotope are there when the activity is 50 Bq?

4 Use the equation $\dfrac{\Delta N}{\Delta t} = -\lambda N$ to explain why the activity of a radioactive nuclide follows the same pattern of decay as the number of undecayed nuclei N.

▶ This shows that you must convert λ into s^{-1} when the activity is in Bq (i.e. decays per second). Don't mix the units!

Radioactive decay equations

The decay of a radioactive substance is like the discharge of a capacitor: both follow an exponential pattern. The rate of decay depends on the **half-life** of the radioactive substance. The half-life is related to the decay constant.

The decay equation

The pattern of exponential decay described on the previous page has a mathematical form. There are three versions of the decay equation, depending on whether you are dealing with activity, number of undecayed nuclei or corrected count rate:

$$\text{activity: } \frac{\Delta N}{\Delta t} = \left(\frac{\Delta N_0}{\Delta t} \right) e^{-\lambda t}$$

$$\text{undecayed nuclei: } N = N_0 e^{-\lambda t}$$

$$\text{corrected count rate: } C = C_0 e^{-\lambda t}$$

Worked example

A sample of a radioactive nuclide initially consists of 3.0×10^6 undecayed nuclei. How many will remain undecayed after 1 hour? The decay constant λ for this nuclide is 1.0×10^{-3} s^{-1}.

Step 1 Write down what you know, and what you want to know:

$$N_0 = 3.0 \times 10^6, \ \lambda = 1.0 \times 10^{-3} \text{ s}^{-1}, \ t = 1 \text{ h} = 3600 \text{ s}, \ N = ?$$

Step 2 Write down the appropriate form of the decay equation:

$$N = N_0 e^{-\lambda t}$$

> ▶ Note that t must have the same units as $1/\lambda$.

Step 3 Substitute and solve, calculating the value of $-\lambda t$ first:

$$N = 3.0 \times 10^6 \exp(-1.0 \times 10^{-3} \text{ s}^{-1} \times 3600 \text{ s}) = 3.0 \times 10^6 \exp(-3.6) = 82\ 000$$

Note that the answer is given to 2 significant figures; because of the randomness of radioactive decay, we cannot say that 81 971 nuclei will remain after 1 hour.

✓ *Quick check 1*

Half-life and decay constant

The **half-life** (symbol $T_{1/2}$) of a radioactive nuclide is the mean (average) time for half the number of nuclei of that nuclide to decay.

We have to say *mean time*, since every measurement will give a slightly different value, as a result of random fluctuations.

The smaller the decay constant λ, the longer the half-life $T_{1/2}$. These two quantities are related by:

$$T_{1/2} = \frac{0.693}{\lambda}$$

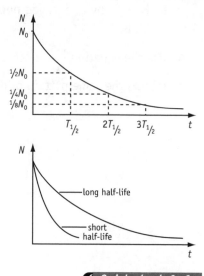

✓ *Quick check 2, 3*

Radiocarbon dating

- Plants take in carbon dioxide from the atmosphere. Some of this contains the radioactive isotope carbon-14 (^{14}C).

- When a plant dies (for example, when a tree is cut down) it ceases to take in CO_2 and the ^{14}C starts to decay, with a half-life of about 5570 years.

- The age of things made from plant material (e.g. wood or cloth) can be estimated by measuring the residual activity, and comparing this with the activity of the same mass of carbon from similar material today.

Worked example

The activity of ^{14}C ($T_{1/2}$ = 5570 years) in a specimen of recently dead wood is 250 Bq kg^{-1}. The activity of a wooden tool from an archaeological dig is 180 Bq kg^{-1}. How old is the tool?

Step 1 Write down what you know, and what you want to know:

$$\frac{\Delta N_0}{\Delta t} = 250 \text{ Bq}, \frac{\Delta N}{\Delta t} = 180 \text{ Bq}, T_{1/2} = 5570 \text{ y}, t = ?$$

Step 2 Use the activity form of the decay equation:

$$\frac{\Delta N}{\Delta t} = \left(\frac{\Delta N_0}{\Delta t}\right)e^{-\lambda t}$$

Substituting the activity values gives

$$e^{-\lambda t} = \frac{180}{250} = 0.72$$

Therefore

$$t = \frac{-(\ln 0.72)}{\lambda} = -(\ln 0.72) \times \frac{T_{1/2}}{0.693} = -(\ln 0.72) \times \frac{5570}{0.693}$$

Step 3 Use a calculator to obtain the result:

$$t = 2640 \text{ y}$$

Storing radioactive waste

Radioactive waste from, for example, nuclear reprocessing plant contains many isotopes with a wide range of half-lives, from a few seconds to thousands of years. High-level waste is very radioactive and produces a great deal of heat. It is vitally important that the storage of this waste takes into account the long half-lives of some of the isotopes. Remember that the half-life is *not* the time for the material to become safe – this is likely to take very many half-lives.

More on the storage of radioactive waste on page 53.

? Quick check questions

1 A particular radioactive nuclide has decay constant 0.03 year^{-1}. A sample has initial activity 40 Bq. What will its activity be after 5 years?

2 Radioactive carbon-14 has a half-life of 5570 years. What is the decay constant for this isotope?

3 A particular nuclide has decay constant 6.0×10^{-3} s^{-1}. What is its half-life? Approximately what fraction of a sample will remain after 200 s?

Nuclear stability

Radioactive decay occurs because the nuclei of some atoms are unstable. In emitting an α or β particle or a γ ray, the nucleus tends towards a more stable state.

The graph of the number of neutrons against the number of protons for all known elements shows that:

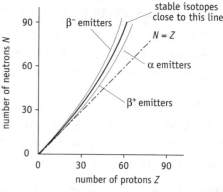

- if a nucleus has a small number of protons, about the same number of neutrons is needed to hold the nucleus together;

- for larger stable nuclei, number of neutrons > number of protons;

- when elements emit α, β^- or β^+ particles the *daughter nuclide* (see below) is nearer the stability line;

- elements above the stability line tend to emit β^- particles;

- elements below the stability line tend to emit β^+ particles.

Types of decay

The notation for an isotope is $^A_Z X$, where A is the number of nucleons (protons + neutrons) and Z is the number of protons. An isotope may decay to form one or more so-called **daughter** products. What happens to A and Z in this process depends on the type of decay.

α decay

An α particle is identical to a helium nucleus, written $^4_2 He$ or $^4_2 \alpha$. The daughter product of $^A_Z X$ has A reduced by 4, and Z reduced by 2. For example:

$$^{232}_{90} Th \ \rightarrow \ ^{228}_{88} Ra \ + \ ^4_2 \alpha$$

β^- decay

In β^- decay, a neutron changes into a proton and an electron. The electron is ejected at high speed as a β^- particle, written $^0_{-1} \beta$ or $^0_{-1} e$. The daughter has A unchanged, and Z increased by 1. For example:

$$^{228}_{88} Ra \ \rightarrow \ ^{228}_{89} Ac \ + \ ^0_{-1} \beta$$

β^+ decay

In β^+ decay, a proton changes into a neutron and a positron (same mass as an electron, same charge as a proton). The positron is ejected as a positively charged beta (β^+) particle, written $^0_{+1} \beta$ or $^0_{+1} e$. The daughter has A unchanged, and Z decreased by 1. For example:

$$^{22}_{11} Na \ \rightarrow \ ^{22}_{10} Ne \ + \ ^0_{+1} \beta$$

Electron capture

A proton in the nucleus can capture an orbiting electron from one of the inner electron 'shells', and they combine to form a neutron. No particle is emitted from the nucleus, but an X-ray photon is emitted from the atom. The daughter has A unchanged, and Z decreased by 1. For example:

$$^{51}_{24}Cr + ^{0}_{-1}e \rightarrow ^{51}_{23}V$$

✓ Quick check 1, 2

Gamma ray emission

After α or β emission the daughter nucleus is often in an excited (unstable) state and can return to a more stable state by losing energy in the form of a photon of γ radiation. There is no change in A or Z when γ is emitted. For example:

$$^{241}_{95}Am \rightarrow ^{237}_{93}Np + ^{4}_{2}\alpha + \gamma$$

Sometimes there is a delay between the emission of α or β and the release of γ. During this time the nucleus is in a **metastable** (m) state. For example, in the production of ^{99m}technetium (^{99m}Tc) from molybdenum ($^{99}_{42}$Mo):

$$^{99}_{42}Mo \rightarrow ^{99m}_{43}Tc + ^{0}_{-1}\beta$$

then:

$$^{99m}_{43}Tc \rightarrow ^{99}_{43}Tc + \gamma$$

The metastable isotope $^{99m}_{43}$Tc is useful in medical imaging (forming computer pictures of parts of the body) because:

- it has a half-life of 6 hours – long enough for diagnosis but not too long for unnecessary exposure;
- it emits only γ, which can be detected by a gamma camera, and is safer inside the body than α or β emitters;
- it can be produced in a hospital more or less on demand from a weekly delivery of molybdenum.

❓ Quick check questions

1 Write down equations to represent the following nuclear decays:

   a A polonium nucleus $^{218}_{84}$Po emits an α particle to become an isotope of lead Pb.

   b A potassium nucleus $^{42}_{19}$K decays by beta (β^-) emission to become an isotope of calcium Ca. A γ photon is also emitted.

   c A fluorine nucleus $^{18}_{9}$F decays by beta (β^+) emission to become an isotope of oxygen O.

   d An iron nucleus $^{55}_{26}$Fe decays by electron capture to become an isotope of manganese Mn.

2 A nucleus of $^{235}_{92}$U decays to $^{223}_{88}$Ra. How many alpha (α) particles and negative beta (β^-) particles are emitted?

Probing matter

In Module 1 we saw how the α particle scattering experiment led to the discovery of the atomic nucleus. The *radius* of the nuclei of elements has been measured by the scattering of α particles, electrons and other particles by target nuclei.

Bombarding radiation or particle

- Ideally the bombarding particle has a small mass compared to the mass of the target nucleus, so the nucleus effectively remains at rest.

- Particles with very high energies act as waves and are diffracted when incident on target nuclei.

- Charged particles (e.g. α particles, electrons) can be accelerated to high speeds by particle accelerators. The smaller the particle mass, the higher the kinetic energy achieved.

- The use of electrons is more reliable than that of α particles because high-energy α particles interact with nuclei by the strong nuclear force. (This is the force that holds nucleons together.) Electrons do not interact with this force.

Closest approach of α particle

An α particle travelling head-on towards a nucleus, with kinetic energy E_K, approaches the nucleus and slows down. At its closest distance r it stops momentarily. All its kinetic energy has been converted to potential energy (E_P):

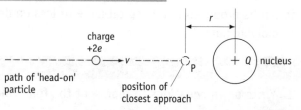

$$E_P = \text{potential at P} \times \text{charge on } \alpha \text{ particle}$$

$$= \left(\frac{1}{4\pi\varepsilon_0 r}\right)Q \times 2e$$

> Both the α particle and the nucleus are positively charged, so they repel.

▶▶ *Remind yourself of electric potential – page 41.*

Rearranging, and using $E_K = E_P$:

$$r = \frac{2Qe}{4\pi\varepsilon_0 E_K}$$

In Rutherford's experiment the α particles had $E_K = 7.68$ MeV $= 1.23 \times 10^{-12}$ J and the target was gold, where:

Q = charge on a gold nucleus = $79 \times 1.60 \times 10^{-19}$ C (for gold $Z = 79$)

e = charge on electron = 1.60×10^{-19} C

$\varepsilon_0 = 8.85 \times 10^{-12}$ F m^{-1}

▶▶ *See Revise AS Physics, page 2, for details of Rutherford's experiment.*

Using these values we get $r = 2.96 \times 10^{-14}$ m. This is *not* the radius of the nucleus, but it gives an idea of the *order of magnitude* of the radius (10^{-14} m).

Faster α particles give a smaller r. If faster and faster α particles are used there comes a point where the number of α particles deflected through a given angle does not agree with theoretical values, because the α particles have *just* penetrated the nucleus itself, i.e. P is just inside the nucleus. r is then the nuclear radius.

✓ *Quick check 1*

Electron diffraction

Another way of estimating the radius of the nucleus is by analysing the *diffraction* pattern that results from high-speed electrons interacting with nuclei.

▶ *More on electron diffraction in Revise AS Physics, page 18.*

We apply the same theory as that used for the diffraction of light waves by a spherical object. The diffraction pattern is a series of light and dark rings.

The first minimum of the scattered intensity occurs at an angle θ to the incident electron beam, where θ is given by

$$\sin \theta = 0.61\lambda/R$$

λ is the **de Broglie wavelength** of the electrons and R is the radius of the nucleus.

▶▶ *More on this also in Revise AS Physics, page 18.*

For diffraction to occur, the wavelength λ must be very small – about the same size as the diameter of the nucleus. For λ to be so small E has to be very high, so the electrons must be accelerated to very high speeds. For high electron energies, $\lambda = hc/E$.

The nucleus is assumed to be spherical, although it doesn't have a well-defined edge.

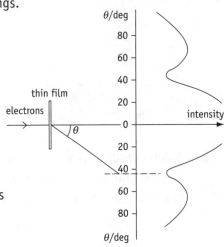

Nuclear radius

Results from α particle scattering and electron diffraction experiments support the relationship between the nuclear radius R and the nucleon or mass number A:

$$R = r_0 A^{1/3}$$

where r_0 lies between 1.2×10^{-15} m and 1.5×10^{-15} m.

Units   Nuclear radii are often expressed in *femtometres* (fm): 1 fm = 1×10^{-15} m.

✓ *Quick check 2–4*

? Quick check questions

1 An α particle of kinetic energy 6.8 MeV travels directly towards a gold nucleus ($Z = 79$). Estimate its closest distance of approach to the gold nucleus.

2 Calculate the radius of an α particle, expressing your answer in fm.

3 The radius of a uranium nucleus is 8.5 fm. Using your answer to Question 2, if an α particle is to just make contact with the uranium nucleus, what is the distance, in fm, between their centres?

4 Calculate the wavelength associated with electrons of energy 500 MeV. These electrons are incident on target nuclei and are diffracted. The angle θ between the incident beam and the first minimum of the scattered intensity is 50°. Assuming the relation $\sin \theta = \dfrac{0.61\lambda}{R}$, estimate the radius R of a target nucleus. ($h = 6.6 \times 10^{-34}$ J s; $c = 3.0 \times 10^8$ m s^{-1}.)

An α particle is a helium nucleus, $A = 4$.

Module 5: end-of-module questions

1 a Complete the table comparing α, β and γ radiation. The data concerning the proton is to enable you to give relative masses and charges. (6)

Type of radiation	Relative mass	Relative charge	Approximate range in air
α			
β⁻			
γ			

proton	1	+1	

b A detector of α, β and γ radiation is placed 20 cm from a radioactive source, and the count rate is recorded. By referring to the properties of α, β and γ radiation, explain the following observations:

  i The count rate falls when a 3 mm thick sheet of aluminium is placed in front of and close to the source. (2)

  ii With the aluminium plate still in place, the count rate remains unchanged when a strong magnetic field is applied in the region between the source and the detector. (1)

c Explain why it is impossible, from the observations in **b**, for you to be completely sure of the types of radiation emitted from the source. (2)

2 a State one way in which γ radiation differs from α and β radiation. (1)

b The diagram shows an experimental arrangement for investigating variation of count rate with distance from a small radioactive source that emits γ radiation.

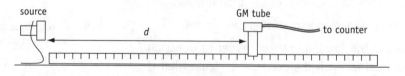

Distance d from source	cm	10	20	30	40
Count rate	min⁻¹	1955	506	245	143

Some of the results obtained are given in the table. The background count was 25 min⁻¹ and has not been taken into account in the table.

  i State two sources of background radiation. (2)

    ii Without plotting a graph, show that the variation in count rate with distance follows an inverse square law. (2)

3 a A radioactive nuclide of potassium is represented by the symbol $^{42}_{19}K$. In the nucleus of such an atom, how many protons are there, and how many neutrons? (2)

  b This nuclide decays by beta (β^-) decay to an isotope of calcium (Ca). Write an equation to represent this decay. (2)

  c The half-life of this isotope of potassium is 12.5 h. Calculate its decay constant. (2)

4 A sample of a radioactive substance has an initial activity of 50 Bq. Its decay constant is 3×10^{-3} s^{-1}. (2)

  a Write an equation to represent how the activity of the sample will change with time. (1)

  b Determine the activity of the sample after 500 s. (2)

  c A Geiger counter is held near the sample. The count rate detected by the counter is less than the sample's activity. State *two* factors that contribute to this. (2)

5 The decay of radon-222 to lead-210 is shown in the figure.

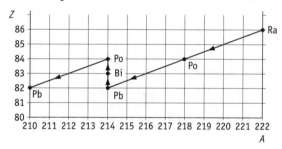

  a For the $^{222}_{86}Ra$ nucleus, state

    i the number of neutrons

    ii the number of protons. (2)

  b **i** State the particle emitted when $^{222}_{86}Ra$ decays into $^{218}_{84}Po$.

    ii Write down the equation representing this decay. (3)

  c **i** State the particle emitted when $^{214}_{82}Pb$ decays into $^{214}_{83}Bi$.

    ii Write down the equation representing this decay. (3)

  d $^{218}_{84}Po$ (polonium) has a half-life of 3 minutes. Calculate the percentage of the polonium atoms that are present at a particular time that will remain after a further 12 minutes. (2)

6 a The graph shows the variation of the neutron number N with proton number Z for naturally occurring stable nuclei.

Copy the graph and mark the typical positions of unstable nuclei that would become more stable by emitting

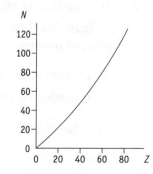

      i an α particle (label this **A**)

      ii a β^- particle (label this **B**)

      iii a β^+ particle (label this **C**).   (3)

b State the changes in N and Z, if any, that result from the emission of

      i an α particle

      ii a γ ray photon.   (3)

c Explain why, in a naturally occurring radioactive series such as that shown in question 5, decays with both α and β^- emissions take place.   (1)

7 a Write down an equation to represent a fluorine ($^{18}_{9}$F) nucleus that decays by β^+ emission to become an isotope of sodium (Na).   (2)

b A copper ($^{64}_{29}$Cu) nucleus decays to an isotope of nickel ($^{64}_{28}$Ni).

This can be represented by the equation

$$^{64}_{29}\text{Cu} + {}^{0}_{-1}\text{e} \rightarrow {}^{64}_{28}\text{Ni}$$

State the name given to this type of decay and explain how it occurs.   (3)

8 Technetium-99m ($^{99m}_{43}$Tc) has a half-life of 6 h and decays by γ emission only. It is used as a tracer in medicine.

a   **i** Explain what is meant by *half-life*.

      ii State what happens to the nucleon and proton numbers when a $^{99m}_{43}$Tc nucleus emits a γ photon.   (3)

b A patient is to be injected with a dose of technetium-99m.

      i Why is a γ emitter preferred to a β or α emitter?

      ii State one advantage and one disadvantage of using an isotope with a half-life of 6 h over one with a much shorter half-life.   (3)

c When the patient is injected, the technetium-99m activity is 2.9×10^8 Bq. Determine the activity 24 h later, assuming all the technetium-99m remains in the body.   (3)

9 a The radius R, in m, of a nucleus of mass number A is given by the formula
$$R = 1.4 \times 10^{-15}A^{1/3}$$

Calculate the radius of a gold ($^{197}_{79}$Au) nucleus.   (2)

b An α particle of radius 2.2×10^{-15} m is travelling head-on towards a gold nucleus. The α particle comes momentarily to rest when it is just on the point of penetrating the gold nucleus.

      i Determine the distance between the centres of the gold nucleus and the α particle when the α particle comes to rest.

      ii Calculate the initial kinetic energy of the α particle.   (4)

Appendix 1: Formulae for question papers

In end-of-module question papers, you will be supplied with a Data Sheet. Except for the equations and relationships listed below, equations will either be provided on the Data Sheet or given in the questions.

It is a good idea to make yourself familiar with the Data Sheet so that you know what will be provided in the examination. The Data Sheet is for both AS and A2, including all the options. The formulae you are expected to learn and recall for Modules 1 to 5 are given below. Questions requiring derivations will not be set for any equations in Modules 4 and 5.

Modules 1–3 (AS)

speed, $v = \dfrac{\Delta s}{\Delta t}$

force, $F = ma$

acceleration, $a = \dfrac{\Delta v}{\Delta t} = \dfrac{v - u}{t}$

momentum, $p = mv$

work done, $W = F \times s \cos\theta$

power, $P = \dfrac{\Delta W}{\Delta t}$

weight $= mg$

kinetic energy, $E_K = \frac{1}{2}mv^2$

change in potential energy, $\Delta E_P = mg\Delta h$

pressure, $p = \dfrac{F}{A}$

the gas law, $pV = nRT$

density, $\rho = \dfrac{m}{V}$

charge, $\Delta Q = I\,\Delta t$

potential difference, $V = IR = \dfrac{W}{Q}$

electrical power, $P = VI$

resistance, $R = \dfrac{\rho l}{A}$

energy, $W = VIt$

Modules 4 and 5 (A2)

speed, frequency and wavelength, $v = f\lambda$

centripetal force, $F = \dfrac{mv^2}{r}$

capacitance, $C = \dfrac{Q}{V}$

inverse square law for force:

gravitational fields, $F = \dfrac{Gm_1 m_2}{r^2}$

electric fields,

$$F = \dfrac{Q_1 Q_2}{4\pi\varepsilon_0 r^2}$$

Appendix 2: Accuracy and errors

Physicists try to make their observations as accurate as possible. Errors in measurements arise in a number of ways and, as an experimentalist, you should try to minimise errors.

Systematic errors

These can arise in a number of ways:

- **Zero error:** e.g. an ammeter does not read zero when no current is flowing through it. If it reads +0.05 A, all of its readings will be too high. Either correct the meter to read zero, or adjust all readings to take account of the error.
- **Incorrect calibration** of an instrument: e.g. an ammeter that reads zero when no current flows, but all other readings are consistently too low or too high. It may read 9.9 A when 10.0 A is flowing. Again, either correct the meter, or adjust all readings.
- **Incorrect use** of an instrument: e.g. screwing a micrometer too tightly, or viewing a meniscus from an angle. Learn the correct technique for using instruments and apparatus.
- **Human reaction:** e.g. when starting and stopping a stopclock. You may always press the button a fraction of a second after the event.

Systematic errors can be reduced or even eliminated. This increases the accuracy of the final result.

Random errors

These often arise as a result of judgements made by the experimenter:

- **Reading from a scale.** You may have to judge where a meter needle is on a scale – what is the nearest scale mark? What fraction of a division is nearest to the needle?
- **Timing a moving object.** When did it start to move? When did it pass the finishing line? You have to judge.

The conditions under which the measurement is made can vary:

- **Equipment** can vary. One trolley may have more friction than another. Two apparently identical resistors may have slightly different values.
- **Samples of materials** may be different. Two lengths of wire from the same reel may have slightly different compositions.
- **Conditions** can vary. Room temperature may change and affect your results.

Some measurements are intrinsically random:

- **Radioactive decay.** If you measure the background radiation in the laboratory for 30 s, you are likely to find slightly different values each time.

Random errors can be reduced, but it is usually impossible to eliminate them entirely. Reducing random errors increases the precision of the final result.

Reducing random errors

Here are some ways to reduce random errors.

- **Make multiple measurements**, and find the mean (average). Roughly speaking, taking four measurements reduces the error by half; 100 measurements will divide the error by 10.
- **Plot a graph**, and draw a smooth curve or a straight line through the points.
- **Choose a suitable instrument** to reduce errors of judgement, e.g. using light gates and an electronic timer instead of timing with a stopwatch. You need to think critically about the instrument: does it introduce other sources of error?

Expressing errors

Here are two ways in which the error or uncertainty in a final result can be expressed.

- **Use significant figures:** a calculation may give $R = 127 \ \Omega$. If the errors are small, you may wish to quote this as $130 \ \Omega$; if the errors are large, as $100 \ \Omega$.
- **Use ± errors:** by considering the errors in individual measurements, you may be able to show the degree of uncertainty in the above result. Small error: $R = (127 \pm 2) \ \Omega$; larger error: $R = (130 \pm 10) \ \Omega$.

Summary

- Think critically about the equipment and methods you use.
- Reduce random errors to increase the precision of your results.
- Reduce systematic errors to increase the accuracy of your results.
- Indicate the extent of error or uncertainty in individual results, and in the final result.

Appendix 3: SI units

The SI system of units is based on seven **fundamental** or **base units**. They are listed in **Table 1** below, together with the quantity of which each is the unit.

You should be familiar with all of these units except the candela.

Most quantities are expressed in **derived units**. For example, area is given in m^2, acceleration in $m\ s^{-2}$. Some derived units are given special names, such as hertz or weber. Some of these are listed in **Table 2** opposite.

It is often useful to be able to express these derived units in terms of other units. This is shown in the fourth column of the table. The fifth column shows the formulae that relate the corresponding quantities.

Sometimes it is easier to remember the relationship between units, e.g. one volt is one joule per coulomb. At other times it is easier to remember the relationship between quantities, e.g. $F = BIl$. It is a great help if you can translate between quantities and units. Then you need only remember half as many formulae.

Table 3 lists the commonly used **prefixes**, e.g. $1\ \mu F = 1$ microfarad $= 10^{-6}$ F.

Table 1 Fundamental SI units

quantity	unit	abbreviation
mass	kilogram	kg
length	metre	m
time	second	s
temperature	kelvin	K
current	ampere	A
amount of substance	mole	mol
luminous intensity	candela	cd

Table 2 Derived SI units

quantity	unit	abbreviation	in terms of other units	equation
frequency	hertz	Hz	s^{-1}	$f = 1/T$
force	newton	N	$kg\ m\ s^{-2}$	$F = ma$
energy, work	joule	J	N m	$W = Fd$
power	watt	W	$J\ s^{-1}$	$P = W/t$
charge	coulomb	C	A s	$Q = It$
p.d., e.m.f.	volt	V	$J\ C^{-1}$	$W = QV$
resistance	ohm	Ω	$V\ A^{-1}$	$V = IR$
capacitance	farad	F	$C\ V^{-1}$	$Q = CV$
magnetic flux density	tesla	T	$N\ A^{-1}\ m^{-1}$ $Wb\ m^{-2}$	$F = BIl$ $\phi = AB$
magnetic flux	weber	Wb	V s	$E = d\phi/dt$
Celsius temperature	degree Celsius	°C	K	$T = \theta + 273$
activity	becquerel	Bq	s^{-1}	$A = dN/dt$

Table 3 Prefixes

factor	prefix	symbol
10^{9}	giga-	G
10^{6}	mega-	M
10^{3}	kilo-	k
10^{-1}	deci-	d
10^{-2}	centi-	c
10^{-3}	milli-	m
10^{-6}	micro-	μ
10^{-9}	nano-	n
10^{-12}	pico-	p
10^{-15}	femto-	f

Answers to quick check questions

Module 4: Waves, fields and nuclear energy

Block 4A

Simple harmonic motion, pages 6–7

1 5 cm; 5 s; 0.2 Hz
2 0.87 s; 1.15 Hz
3 20 Hz; 0.05 s

More about SHM, pages 8–9

1
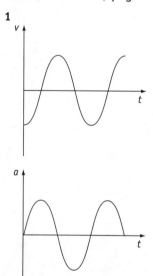

2 40 mm; 0.1 Hz; –40 mm
3 $x = 0.2\cos \pi t$; 0.12 m
4 24 mm s^{-1}
5 at midpoint; at ends of oscillation

Energy changes, damping and resonance, pages 10–11

1 E_k
2 decreases
3 useful: e.g. wind instrument, radio tuner
   not useful: e.g. booming loudspeaker; oscillating bridge

Representing waves, pages 12–13

1 sound longitudinal, others transverse
2 transverse
3 light waves and microwaves

Wave quantities, pages 14–15

1 p = amplitude = 5 cm; q = wavelength = 4 m
2 0.50 s; 0.50 ms; 2.0 μs
3
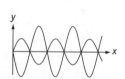

4 45 mm s^{-1}
5 30 kHz

Interference and diffraction, pages 16–17

1 single wave of same wavelength, 3 times the amplitude

2
3 dimmer (less light); more spread out
4 yes, if joined to same vibrating source

Young's double-slit experiment, pages 18–19

1 D (2 or 3 m); s (about 0.5 mm); w (a few mm); λ (400 to 700 nm)
2 path difference = (integer + ½) × wavelength
3 halved
4 556 nm; error (uncertainty) in all measurements

Superposition and stationary waves, pages 20–21

1
   1.2 m
2 30 mm
3 Displacements are always equal and opposite.
4 0.80 m; 320 m s^{-1}

The diffraction grating, pages 22–23

1 5.2°; 10.4°

2 11

3 **a** more spread out

  b closer

  c same separation but dimmer

Block 4B

Capacitors, pages 24–25

1 8.0 μF; 160 μC

2 2.0 μF; 40 mJ

3 the same (100 s)

Discharging a capacitor, pages 26–27

1 graph 1 – bigger R, so takes longer

2 2.0×10^{-9} C; 4.0×10^{-10} C

3 0.24 mA; 0.089 mA

4 10 ms

Block 4C

Describing circular motion, pages 28–29

1 2π; π; $\pi/2$ or 1.57; $\pi/3$ or 1.05; $\pi/4$ or 0.79

2 57.3°; 14.3°; 180°; 360°; 36°

3 524 s; 44 s

4 75.4 rad s^{-1}

5 0.23 m s^{-1}

Centripetal acceleration and force, pages 30–31

1 friction with road (and contact force with road, if not horizontal)

2 97 N

3 smaller r, so larger F

4 1700 m s^{-1}

Gravitational fields, pages 32–33

1 change in g not noticeable; change in g enough to decrease weight; large change in g so significant decrease in weight

2 8 N

3 530 N

4 3.6 N kg^{-1}

Gravitational potential, pages 34–35

1 860 J kg^{-1}

2 -2.92×10^{6} J kg^{-1}

3 23 800 J

4 about 1.0 N kg^{-1}

Planets and satellites, pages 36–37

1 **a** 2.36×10^{6} s

  b 3.83×10^{6} m

2 7600 m s^{-1}; 5800 s

3 4.5×10^{5} m

Electric fields, pages 38–39

1 parallel, equally spaced lines

2 1.6×10^{-15} N

3 300 V m^{-1} (or N C^{-1})

4 $E \propto V$; $E \propto 1/d$, so E = 20 000 V m^{-1}

5 1.92 N

Coulomb's law, pages 40–41

1 equal and opposite repulsive forces

2 230 N

3 1.4×10^{11} N C^{-1}

Block 4D

Electromagnetic forces, pages 42–43

1 0.80 N

2 1.6×10^{-13} N

3 up out of paper

4 5.7×10^{-4} m

5 the faster electron in each case

Electromagnetic induction, pages 44–45

1 0.2 T

2 0.079 Wb

3 0.52 V

4 the first two

5 0.165 V

Block 4E

Mass–energy conservation, pages 46–47

1 1.009 u

2 mass of neutron > mass of proton + neutron; more mass–energy needed

3 4.4×10^{9} kg s^{-1}

4 mass of products < mass of mother

Fusion and fission, pages 48–49

1 mass ($^{2}_{1}$H + $^{3}_{1}$H) – mass ($^{4}_{2}$He + $^{1}_{0}$n) = 0.031×10^{-27} kg

  = 17.4 MeV

2 fusion (17.4 MeV per 5 nucleons compared to 200 MeV per 235 nucleons)

Thermal nuclear reactors and transmutation, pages 50–51

1 More energy is released per kg, more fissions occur per second; therefore the reactor is hotter and more efficient.

2 **a** Moderator slows neutrons.

   b Coolant cools reactor and carries thermal energy to water to produce steam.

   c Control rods absorb neutrons to control rate of fission.

Nuclear safety, pages 52–53

1 Answer in terms of: risk of accident/hijack/terrorist attack; weight to be carried; possible damage to environment; ability to contain radioactivity or recover flask in case of accident.

2 taken from reactor → cooling pond → placed in flask → transported to reprocessing plant → cooling pond → casing stripped off → waste separated from useful isotopes → waste vitrified → stored → stored underground

Module 5: Nuclear instability

Block 5A

Radioactivity, pages 60–61

1 Radiation passes through magnetic field – not deflected.

2 γ

Background radiation and the inverse square law, pages 62–63

1 cosmic rays, nuclear test fallout, soil, rocks

2 8 counts per 10 s

3 112 counts s^{-1}

4 410 counts per 10 s

The decay constant, pages 64–65

1 presence of background radiation; sample radiates in all directions, so not all decays detected

2 1.2×10^{-6} s^{-1}

3 **a** 1.7×10^{-6} s^{-1}

   b 29×10^{6}

4 $\frac{\Delta N}{\Delta t} \propto N$, so $\frac{\Delta N}{\Delta t}$ decreases as N decreases

Radioactive decay equations, pages 66–67

1 34 Bq

2 1.24×10^{-4} $year^{-1}$

3 116 s; approx. 3/10

Block 5B

Nuclear stability, pages 68–69

1 **a** $^{218}_{84}\text{Po} \rightarrow {}^{214}_{82}\text{Pb} + {}^{4}_{2}\alpha$

   b $^{42}_{19}\text{K} \rightarrow {}^{42}_{20}\text{Ca} + {}^{0}_{-1}\beta$; then $^{42}_{20}\text{Ca} \rightarrow {}^{42}_{20}\text{Ca} + \gamma$

   c $^{18}_{9}\text{F} \rightarrow {}^{18}_{8}\text{O} + {}^{0}_{+1}\beta$

   d $^{55}_{26}\text{Fe} + {}^{0}_{-1}\text{e} \rightarrow {}^{55}_{25}\text{Mn}$

2 3 α and 2 β^{-}

Probing matter, pages 70–71

1 3.35×10^{-14} m

2 2.2 fm

3 10.7 fm

4 2.49×10^{-15} m; 1.98×10^{-15} m

Answers to end-of-module questions

Module 4: Waves, fields and nuclear energy

Pages 55–58

1 **a** motion where acceleration is proportional to displacement from fixed point and directed towards it

    b **i** 0.06 m **ii** 1.2 s **iii** 0.83 Hz

       iv 1.6 m s^{-2} **v** 0.31 m s^{-1}

    c, d

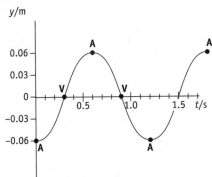

2 **a** Resonance happens when forcing frequency = natural frequency and maximum amplitude vibrations occur.

    b

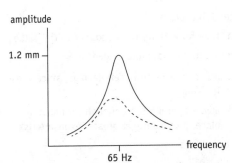

    c friction introduced to reduce amplitude

    d See dotted line in **b**.

3 **a** A bright fringe is formed where two waves, one from each slit, meet and interfere constructively. Path difference between them must be a whole number of wavelengths.

    b 1.3 mm

    c Single-slit diffraction pattern would be seen – broad central band of light getting dimmer away from centre.

4 **a** transverse, as displacement perpendicular to velocity

    b 1.2 m s^{-1}

    c 2.0 cm

    d It could (since transverse waves can be polarised) by restricting the plane of vibration of the string, e.g. to up and down.

5 **a** 2.5 V

    b slope = $\dfrac{10\ \mu C}{18\ s}$ = 0.56 μA

    c $R = \dfrac{V}{I} = \dfrac{2.5}{0.56 \times 10^{-6}}$ = 4.5 MΩ

    d $\tau = 20$ s; $R = \dfrac{\tau}{C}$ = 5.0 MΩ

    e Time constant method: drawing tangent incurs greater uncertainty than reading time at 3.7 μC.

6 **a** 20 μA

    b 0.02 C

    c 1000 s

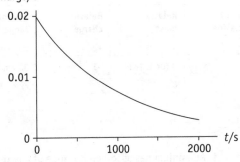

    d

    e 0.012 C

7 **a** **i** $F = \dfrac{Gm_1m_2}{r^2}$ **ii** the same

    b 13 500 m s^{-1}

    c 91 days

8 **a** The work done per unit mass in bringing a small mass from infinity to that point

    b Infinity is taken as zero potential. An object in any gravitational field will have less than zero potential.

    c 5.75 × 10^{10} J

9 **a** **i** 500 × 10^3 V m^{-1} **ii** 5.0 × 10^{-11} N **iii** 125 m s^{-2}

    b downward force on dust particle

    c constant acceleration downwards, constant velocity horizontally, therefore path parabolic

10 a force downwards

    b 1.0 T

11 a flux = 3.0×10^{-4} Wb; flux linkage = 0.03 Wb

b no e.m.f. induced in vertical sides; e.m.f.s induced in top and bottom sides oppose, so no resultant e.m.f.

c 0.38 V

12 a When two light nuclei fuse, binding energy per nucleon of resulting heavy nucleus is greater than for the two light nuclei; therefore energy is released.

b 5.49 MeV (8.78×10^{-13} J)

13 a **i** Neutron captured by (heavy) nucleus which splits and produces neutrons. Neutrons in turn split other nuclei, producing more neutrons, and so on.

ii Smallest mass that will self-sustain a chain reaction, i.e. so that each fission gives rise to at least one other.

iii Control rods, which absorb neutrons, are lowered into reactor to slow down rate of reaction, or raised to increase rate of reaction.

b stored in cooling ponds → transported to processing plant → stored under water → cladding removed → spent fuel separated into waste and useful products. Waste disposed by sealing in cement or glass and stored in special repositories, eventually stored underground.

Module 5: Nuclear instability

Pages 72–74

1 a

Type of radiation	Relative mass	Relative charge	Approx. range in air
α	4	+2	few cm
β^-	0 (or 1/1860)	−1	30 cm
γ	0	0	many km

proton	1	+1	

b **i** Aluminium has absorbed β (range of any α too short to reach detector).

ii Any γ emitted from source is unaffected, since not charged; if no γ, only background present, which is also unaffected.

c Test for α has not been done. Also, unless background known or detector moved, no way of telling whether γ present.

2 a Example answer: γ is electromagnetic radiation, α and β are particles. (Other answers acceptable)

b **i** cosmic radiation; naturally occurring radon in soil/rocks

ii Take 25 s^{-1} from each count. Count at 20 cm is about ¼ of count at 10 cm, and count at 40 cm is about ¼ that at 20 cm.

3 a 19 protons, 23 neutrons

b $^{42}_{19}\text{K} \rightarrow {}^{42}_{20}\text{Ca} + {}^{0}_{-1}\beta$

c $\lambda = 0.055$ day^{-1}

4 a $\dfrac{\Delta N}{\Delta t} = \left(\dfrac{\Delta N_0}{\Delta t}\right)e^{-\lambda t}$

b 11.2 Bq

c Source emits in all directions; counter may not detect all radiation that enters it.

5 a **i** 136 **ii** 86

b **i** α **ii** $^{222}_{86}\text{Ra} \rightarrow {}^{218}_{84}\text{Po} + {}^{4}_{2}\alpha$

c **i** β **ii** $^{214}_{82}\text{Pb} \rightarrow {}^{214}_{83}\text{Bi} + {}^{0}_{-1}\beta$

d 6.25%

6 a

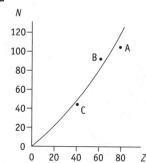

b **i** N down by 4, Z down by 2 **ii** no change

c to enable nuclei after decay to progressively reach stability line

7 a $^{18}_{9}\text{F} \rightarrow {}^{18}_{8}\text{Na} + {}^{0}_{+1}\beta$

b electron capture

8 a **i** time for activity to fall to half initial value

ii A and Z remain unchanged

b **i** less risk of internal cell damage, since γ less ionising

ii advantage: 6 h long enough for imaging to take place; disadvantage: greater exposure risk

c 1.8×10^7 Bq

9 a 8.1×10^{-15} m

b **i** 10.3×10^{-15} m **ii** 22 MeV

Index

Note: **bold** page numbers indicate main topics

A

α radiation *see* alpha radiation
absorption experiments 60–1
acceleration
  centripetal **30–1**, 36, 43, 75
  downward 39
  equations 8–9
  formula for 75
  of free fall 32
  particle 70
  vertical, constant 39, 54
AGR (advanced gas-cooled reactor) 51
air columns 21
alpha radiation 60
  closest approach of α particle 70–1
  decay 68
  nuclear transformations 47
  penetrating power 60
  summary table 61
amount of substance (mole) 78
ampere (unit of current) 42, 78
amplitude 6
  waves 14, 16
angular displacement 28
angular speed and frequency 29
antinodes on stationary waves 20, 21
artificial satellites 36–7
artificial transmutation **51**
atomic mass units 46
attractive forces
  electric 38, 54
  see also gravitational
average rate of decay 64, 66

B

ß radiation *see* beta radiation
background radiation and count **62**, 63
becquerel (unit of radioactive decay) 64, 65, 79
beta radiation 51, 60
  decay 68
  penetrating power 61
  summary table 61
binding energy 46, 48
biological shield in thermal nuclear reactors 52
bombarding radiation or particle 70
boron in control rod 51
brightness 18

C

cadmium in control rod 51
candela (unit of luminous intensity) 78
capacitors **24–7**
  charging 25
  formula for capacitance 75
  unit of capacitance (farad) 24, 79
  see also discharging capacitor
car suspension system 10
carbon
  –14 isotope and radiocarbon dating 67
  nucleus 46, 48
  radioactive 65
  in thermal nuclear reactors 51
carbon dioxide as coolant 51
Celsius (temperature) 79
centre of gravity 33
centre of mass 33
centripetal acceleration and force **30–1**, 36, 43, 75
chain reaction 49
changing velocity and constant speed 30
charges
  charged parallel plates 38–9, 54
  charged particle in uniform electric fields, motion of 39, 54
  charging capacitor 25
  force between two 40
  moving, electromagnetic force on 42–3
  objects with *see* electric fields
  point charge, electric field strength for 41, 54
  and radioactivity 61
  stored 24
  unit of *see* coulomb
circular motion **28–9**
  angular displacement 28
  and electromagnetic forces 43
  speed around circular path 28–9
  see also centripetal; sphere
circumference of circle 28
cladding in thermal nuclear reactors 52
coherent waves 17, 18
  see also laser
conductors and electromagnetism 42, 44–5
conservation *see* mass-energy conservation

constant

electric 54
gravitational 33, 54
horizontal speed 39, 54
speed 30, 39, 54
time, capacitance and 25, 27
vertical acceleration 39, 54
see also under decay, radioactive
constructive interference 16, 17
control rods 50–1, 52
coolant rods 50–1, 52
cosine curve 8
cosmic rays 52
coulomb (unit of charge) 24, 38
  force per 38, 54
  newtons per 38, 39
Coulomb's law **40–1**, 54
  electric field strength 41
  electric potential and potential energy 41
  force between two charges 40
count rate 62–3, 64
critical condition and thermal nuclear reactor 50
critical damping 10
critical mass 49
current *see* electric current
curves 8
  charging and discharging 25, 26, 27
cyclotron 43

D

damping **10**
danger, nuclear 60
  see also safety
dating, radiocarbon 67
daughter products 68
de Broglie wavelength 71
decay, radioactive 47
  constant **64–5**
    activity of sample 64
    and half-life 66–7
    pattern of 65
  equations **66–7**
  exponential 26, 65, 66
  per second 64
  radiocarbon dating 67
  random errors 77
  types of **68–9**
  units (becquerel) 64, 65, 79
deflection
  experiments 60
  by magnetic field 61